JOAN OLIPHANT-FRASER, Dame Chevalier de l'Ordre des Coteaux de Champagne, was born in a three-star vintage, one which has been said to combine the finesse and bouquet of 1884 with the body and richness of 1893.

She received a diploma in Oenology in Paris and many magnums later became a Member Judge of the Club Oenologique in England, and is a contributor to the Wheeler's Anthology, *Oysters and Champagne.*

Her other love is movement which embraces all sorts of dancing and in more recent years, as a result of gourmet activities, various types of exercise to keep slender, youthful and supple.

A great believer in deep breathing she is an advocate of fresh air and the outdoor life and can think of nothing better than a simple little meal prepared by a great Chef accompanied by a couple of bottles of de Luxe Champagne lovingly consumed half way up (or down) a mountain.

Described as a Slender Gourmet she would like to spread the word that you can indulge and shed the pounds at the same time.

My life has been a love affair with Champagne
and I would like to dedicate this book
to my favourite ten 'Grandes Marques'

Laurent-Perrier
Roederer
G.H. Mumm
Heidsieck Dry Monopole
Taittinger
Piper Heidsieck
Henriot
Perrier-Jouet
Pol Roger
Charles de Cazanove

JOAN OLIPHANT-FRASER

ROBERT HALE · LONDON

First published in Great Britain 1987
Second edition 1991

ISBN 0 7090 4680 4

Robert Hale Limited
Clerkenwell House
Clerkenwell Green
London EC1R 0HT

Photoset in North Wales by
Derek Doyle & Associates, Mold, Clwyd.
Printed in Great Britain by
St Edmundsbury Press, Bury St Edmunds, Suffolk
and bound by Hunter & Foulis Ltd.

'O! that this too too solid flesh would melt ...'
Hamlet, Act 1, Scene II

Fontaine de Champagne

Contents

The Slender Gourmet

Foreword

The Slender Gourmet Introduces the Champagne Lifestyle

You may well ask, 'Who is the Slender Gourmet' – an apparent contradiction in terms? A sylph? A bon viveur? Both, of course. It is possible and, more important, desirable to have one's gateaux and dance all night.

I have marvellous news for the young in heart, if not in calendar years. Born in a good vintage myself, I conduct a class in Yoga and Aerobics and eat like a filly.

Before I became The Slender Gourmet I was a dancer whose love of the good life was making me less than sylph-like. As I pirouetted to romantic nocturnes by Chopin and gazed into my partner's eyes, visions of little woodcock simmering in rich cream sauces, flambéed with Armagnac, or Crêpes filled with apples soaked in Calvados topped with country fresh clotted cream flashed through my mind.

Like others, I rebelled against the austerity and boredom of dieting and regimented press-ups. I was searching for a pleasurable way to lose a few pounds.

So I studied nutrition and certain facts emerged: a gourmet lifestyle could still be followed provided one observed certain rules which, far from detracting, actually enhance the pleasures of the table.

Not just a glass of bubbles

Champagne has always been my favourite wine. I drank it for breakfast on my sixteenth birthday and I have done so ever since. Then I discovered that it can become part of a successful slimming campaign which includes dining at the best restaurants or preparing special Slender Gourmet dishes at home.

I also decided that the exercises had to reflect the quality of this Champagne lifestyle. They too had to be fun and imaginative and, above all, done in comfortable, pleasing surroundings. Even a mildly vigorous work-out in a Gym should be followed by luxuriating in a whirlpool letting the bubbles pummel away. To be even more imaginative, taking a trip in a hot-air balloon provides an opportunity of breathing deeply of fresh air that helps wonderfully to restore one's joie de vivre.

I have written the Champagne Diet for those of us who have acquired through success, excess or distress a few extra pounds. If you decide to follow this new Epicurean approach to dieting and exercising, not only will you become more lissom and enjoy better health and vitality but a whole new series of interests will evolve.

Nice, but not strictly necessary, accoutrements for the Champagne Diet:

A gold-tipped Palette	see chapter 6
A silver Spoon	see chapter 5
A gentleman with a Diamond Tie-Pin	see chapter 5

Where to find, and how to acquire, the above items will be explained in my next book, *The Champagne Lifestyle*.

1 *A Little Overweight perhaps?*

One morning take a good look at yourself in a full-length mirror. The reflection that half-smiles back is not bad. In fact you could be described as well dressed, but what is *this* that spoils the line of your clothes? It wasn't there when you were twenty. What has happened in the intervening years? You have become successful; in short, too much food and, worse still, too many drinks.

The majority of us are not teetotallers; we drink convivially in wine bars, at lunchtime and with the evening meal. We drink not only when we are thirsty but in order to enjoy ourselves.

A mixture of liquid passes our lips throughout the day and evening ranging from whisky and sodas, gin and tonics, brandy, sherry, port, beer and carbohydrate laden cocktails like pinacoladas, cobblers and punches, not to mention carbonated fruit drinks, all of which can be high in artificial additives and unhealthy sugars.

What we drink is even more fattening than what we eat. If you were to write down every single drink you have during the day it could tot up to an amazing 1,000 calories plus!

Don't Give It Up!

Don't become abstemious – it's bad for the mental equilibrium as well as putting a damper on your life-style. Instead, be selective, keep to one drink only during your dieting period and let that drink be the very best, the Charlemagne of drinks, Champagne.

One other drink is an important accessory to the diet and that is the Champagne Companion, *Aqua Minerale*, which makes the bubbles go further.

Bottled water that comes from natural springs and spas contains lots of healthy minerals and is very different from tap water, which is not only deficient in minerals but can contain small deposits of arsenic. Though a little poison does you good occasionally, acting as a stimulant, it is not part of the Champagne Diet, which has its roots in wholesomeness. As Louis Pasteur, biologist and chemist said, 'Wine is the healthiest of drinks'. Why? Because a pure, unadulterated wine, like Champagne, contains vitamins, minerals, acids and enzymes that keep gourmets healthy and slender. These acids and enzymes also aid the digestion and thorough assimilation of food, preventing it from building up as deposits of fat in the body.

Champagne is perfect as an apéritif. It prepares the gastric juices for the meal ahead. During the meal it helps the metabolism of fats and tranquilizes the digestive system afterwards.

The Champagne Style of Dieting

Champagne contains only 75 calories to a 4 fl. oz glass and the Champagne Companion is calorie free.

When you follow the dietary ratio of 60% water to 40% Champagne, and assuming you might be drinking ten glasses a day, four glasses of Champagne and six of *Aqua Minerale* total only 300 calories, whereas ten assorted drinks could go well over 1,000 leaving you hardly any calories over for the Slender Gourmet style food which is a vital part of the Champagne Diet.

The Slender Gourmet Style of Eating

Food must be of the best. Simple fare like caviar, oysters, smoked salmon, filet steak and asparagus tips are all slimming and nutritious.

Meat pies, french fries, peas or puddings and breakfast of fried eggs and bacon are out on the grounds of being plebeian, fatty, carbohydrate and calorie loaded.

Every meal, whether eaten at home or at one of The Slender Gourmet recommended restaurants must match the excellence of Champagne. The Slender Gourmet's style of eating is a gastronomic adventure.

The Slender Gourmet Style of Exercising

The exercises must be both effective and fun. They can be the result of a leisure pursuit or become a part of your everyday round of activities.

The Champagne style of eating and drinking takes care of the pounds (even stones) and the Slender Gourmet exercises look after the inches.

2 *I Get a Kick from Champagne*

A glass or two of Champagne produces exhilaration without deflation. This is because the bubbles carry the alcohol into the blood stream more quickly than still wines or other drinks. We all need these stimuli, especially if we hit the dietary doldrums.

Cole Porter tried to make us believe he got no kick from Champagne. Quite false, he drank gallons and was just saying that to some lady who thrilled him even more.

What makes Champagne so special?

There is an abundance of sparkling wines on the market but they are not Champagne. The only sparkling wine that can call itself Champagne comes from a small region in the north-east of France around the mountain of Rheims and the Marne Valley stretching south down the Cotes des Blancs. It is here that everything comes together, soil, climate, grape varieties, skill and expertise of the vigneron and Mâitre de Cuvée to produce a great, pure wine.

Grape Varieties

Champagne, although a white wine, is made from both black and white grapes. Three varieties are used which contribute to its character. The Pinot Noir grape gives body and strength; Pinot Meunier, another black grape, gives freshness and youth; Chardonnay, a white grape, contributes finesse and elegance.

Non-Vintage for Everyday Drinking

For everyday drinking non-vintage Champagnes are the most popular, expressing the personality of the Houses that make them. You can expect a consistency of standard and style from year to year. Most Houses refer to their non-vintage as 'Brut' which mean extremely dry.

The best of the Grandes Marques (literally translated as 'big blends') are: Perrier-Jouët, Louis Roederer, G.H. Mumm, Dry Monopole, Piper Heidsieck, Taittinger, Laurent-Perrier, Henriot, Pol Roger and Charles de Cazanove.

It's a matter of taste whether you prefer a soft, light style like Mumm's Cordon Rouge to a bigger wine like Louis Roederer's Brut Premier which has a lot of character and depth for a non-vintage.

Pink Champagne or Rosé

Rosé Champagnes get their colour either from a small addition of still red wine or by leaving the skins of the black Pinot Noir grapes in contact with the 'must' (unfermented grape juice) for a short time.

A young Rosé can be light, fresh, a touch insouciant – perfect for an early morning encounter, whereas, a Rosé that has had a few years in a bottle can mature into a great Champagne with lots of body, fruitiness and character.

In spite of its slightly frivolous image, partly created by film stars of the Twenties, who used it as a bubble bath, Rosé or Pink Champagnes should be taken seriously.

Vintage for Special Occasions

A vintage is only declared in exceptionally good years when the grapes are of a high quality and the Champagne expresses the characteristics of that particular year.

For example, the Laurent Perrier '78 vintage was rounder, richer, more masculine perhaps, than the flowery, fragrant crisp '79.

de Luxe Champagnes

These Crême de la Crême Champagnes are made from the first pressings of the finest grapes.

Apart from the famous Dom Perignon, there are the equally prestigious Laurent Perrier 'Grand Siècle', Louis Roederer 'Cristal', G.H. Mumm 'René Lalou', Heidsieck Dry Monopole 'Diamant Bleu', Taittinger 'Comtes de Champagne', Piper Heidsieck 'Rare', Henriot 'Baccarat', Perrier-Jouët 'Belle Époque'.

When you have become a successful Slender Gourmet, reward yourself with one of these exceptional Champagnes.

The Slimmer's Champagne (The Ultra Brut)

Quietly, unobtrusively, without a big fanfare two Champagne Houses have

bone dry style of bubbly

produced a new style of Champagne which, being completely **SUGAR FREE**, is ideal for slimmers.

It was originally created at the request of jockeys and polo players who have to keep their weight down to a shadow of our more indulgent selves. After a race or match they need either to celebrate or commiserate. In each case, the occasion calls for Champagne.

A horse lover, maintaining that what was good enough for him was good enough for his horse, used to give his steed a tankard of Black Velvet – Guinness and Champagne! A Derby winner, perhaps!

A Slender Gourmet needs to be revived occasionally with the Slimmer's Special, the carbohydrate free, bone-dry type of Champagne.

There is a choice between Laurent-Perrier's Ultra Brut and Piper Heidsieck's Brut Sauvage. Brut Sauvage is a vintage whereas Ultra Brut is a blend of several vintages. Both are excellent; it's a matter of taste which you prefer. Try both to find out.

So Wickedly Delightful

The most popular Champagne in England today is the Brut, but sweet, or Demi-sec Champagnes are still obtainable. Although, as you might have guessed, they are not recommended for Aspiring Slender Gourmets.

Sweet wines were popular during the reign of Louis XV when a much sweeter style of Champagne was preferred. The wide-brimmed saucer glass was originally designed for this full-bodied aromatic wine, into which, the ladies of the court would dip slices of Madeira cake. But, they were not worried about weight. The curvaceous hourglass figure was fashionable and the gentlemen too relied on corsets to hold their manly shapes together.

There may be times, however, when your blood sugar is low and a glass of demi-sec revitalizes the system. If this is the case, Heidsieck Dry Monopole's 'Top Rich' is sweet without being cloying and would marry well with a simple plate of fraises du bois.

Look and Listen – Nose and Taste

When you hold a glass of Champagne up to the light its colour will range from pale straw (suggesting youth) to the golden tones of maturity.

Some people hold the glass to their ear. Cyril Ray, a renowned bon viveur, said 'a great Champagne speaks to you in its bubbles'. 'La Mousse', or the sparkle, consists of a lively flow that delicately explode with a small plop when they reach the surface of the wine, indicating a Champagne of elegance. Should they explode with a noisy pop, dissipate and subside flatly, this could indicate a young, brash wine of little breeding.

The bouquet which you received by nosing the wine, should be fresh and clean, veering towards flowery, fruity aromas.

Often the smell of the wine will be an indicator as to its taste, which should be dry, clean and pleasing. Nuances of flavour ranging from light, crisp, delicate, fruity, full, fragrant will come through, but always there is that refreshing tingle on the tongue that makes Champagne so aristocratic.

A great Champagne will have character, length (extension of flavour) and an aftertaste that lingers on the palate, and, if you are lucky, will remain after the wine is finished.

The Gods on Olympus only had nectar. We mortals are more fortunate in having Champagne.

Champagne and Music

Charles de Cazanove is one of the oldest Houses in Champagne dating back to 1811. Since then his House has supplied wine to the Stately Homes of Europe and England where, amongst other cultural entertainments, the great hostesses of the day held elegant musical soirées. Listening to a Chopin nocturne or Mozart's Violin Concerto whilst gazing at a stream of lively bubbles ascending in a slender flute is conducive to relaxing flights of fancy. For example, what wines go best with what music? A robust Burgundy might accompany a full symphony orchestra playing Beethoven. However, the cannon firing off in the finale of Tchaikovsky's 1812 Overture has been likened to the rumbustious opening of Champagne bottles when corks fly forth with similar nerve-shattering explosions. A practice to be avoided. The cork should leave the bottle with a gentle sigh. This is achieved by slowly turning the bottle against the cork (not the reverse). The cork will gradually ascend and make its departure with a languid 'soupire' like the soft muted note produced on a solo violin.

Champagne, perhaps more than other wines, marries well with light operettas and classic string arrangements, so it is not surprising that when Charles de Cazanove was looking for a suitable name to sum up the exquisite perfection of his new prestigious Cuvée, that he should choose the name of the world's finest violin-maker, Stradivarius.

At the International launch of this new Cuvée which may take place in the *Salle de Chambre* in the cellars of Epernay, or in the ballroom of some great hotel, a string quartet to honour this occasion will play music by famous composers, performed by talented artists to a sparkling audience of Champagneophiles.

Don't Discard Your Empties

Bottles and labels are becoming valuable – I was made an offer for my collection of old, prestigious empties which I use, instead of ornaments or framed photographs, to decorate the sideboard.

Designer Labels

The Taittinger labels designed by famous artists are becoming Collectors' items. Their first label commemorating the '78 vintage was by Hungarian artist Victor Vasarely. Another, celebrating their '81 vintage, was by the French painter Arman who designed a pattern of interlacing violins on a black lacquered background, symbolizing a Muse serenading the liquid stars of Champagne.

Designer Bottles

Many of the great Cuvées come in copies of the original antique-shaped bottles commissioned by the Monarchs and Potentates who ordered them in former times.

A bottle with an elegant shape is Laurent-Perrier's 'Grand Siècle', which is a copy of the original bottle blown by the Master Glassblowers in the reign of the Sun King, Louis XIV.

A particularly lovely bottle is Perrier-Jouët's 'Belle Epoque' decorated with the famous garland of white, or pink, anemones designed by Emile Gallé in 1902. It is a perfect example of Art Nouveau. Today, in fact, empty magnums of Belle Epoque can fetch almost as much money in the flea markets of Paris as the full standard size bottles filled with Champagne!

Conversational Door Stops

The giant sized bottles – Jeroboams which hold two magnums or four bottles; Rehoboams = six bottles; Methuselahs = eight bottles; Salamanazars = twelve bottles; Balthazars = sixteen bottles and the gigantic Nebuchadnezzar = twenty bottles, make 'GREAT', 'GREATER' and 'GREATEST' Door Stops, giving one something stylish on which to stub a big toe, or better still, to make a startling entrance accompanied by a few rich epithets.

3 *The Slender Gourmet Guide to Healthy Eating*

Simple, pure natural foods not only keep you healthy but slender too. This daily eating plan consists of foods rich in fibres, low on fats, veering away from salt and cutting sugars to the minimum.

Meat, game, poultry and fish should come from animals that have followed the Slender Gourmet lifestyle and been allowed to enjoy their natural habitat, eating only the best foods and exercising to keep their weight down. Better to resemble a caribou than a plump partridge.

Grooming the Inner Gourmet

It is important to keep as beautiful and slender within as without but to achieve this a good proportion of fibre or 'roughage' in your diet is essential. Fibre is found in cereals, grains, nuts, fruit, vegetables and salads.

Bread is a high-fibre food providing it is made from wholemeal or wholewheat flour which contains the whole grain. Some gourmet bakers add chopped walnuts, celery and poppy seeds to their recipe which bolsters up the fibre content as well as providing additional flavour and an *al dente* bite.

Bread made from white flour has less flavour and little nutritional value. But worse still, because its texture is soft and aerated, it acts like blotting paper, swelling up with liquid in the stomach. A couple of slices can leave you feeling and looking like the Michelin man for hours.

However, there is an exception – the long, French loaf familiar to us all tucked under the arm of a Parisian bicyclist. The crust compliment cheese, pâtes and breakfast-time marmalade. We know that Aborigines stimulate and massage their gums with twigs. This has a comparable effect. The soft, white centre must be discarded at all costs.

Pasta can help you slim

This is good news for devotees of spaghetti, noodles and rice. Wild rice, the seeds of which come from rare exotic grasses that grow in faraway swamps, is the In Pasta on the Slender Gourmet's Diet. Its distinctive texture and taste mixes well with the brown variety. Other sources of fibre are vegetables, fruit and salads.

A haute-cuisine potato

Do eat potatoes, but, as they have a high starch content, eat them in either of these two Slender Gourmet ways.

Bake the potatoes in their jackets, eat mainly the skins which contain most of the flavour and all the nutrients and discard the white starch in the middle, which birds adore.

Alternatively, Pommes Soufflées, potato balls, hollow in the centre, hot and crisp on the outside, are considered by many gourmets to be the quintessential potato.

Exotic fruit enzymes

Exotic fruits like mango, pineapple, paw paw and passion fruit contain acids and enzymes. When marinated or cooked with pork, beef and other meats and poultry they help to destroy the toxics and fats in the meat's tissues. Sometimes choose recipes or dishes that combine fruit with meats.

Citrus fruit such as lemons, grapefruits or oranges, though acid-tasting in the mouth, are alkaline in the stomach, and are particularly refreshing first thing in the morning when the body's alkaline level is low.

Lock up your lettuces

Both rabbits and gourmets can be forgiven for running away with members of the lettuce family, especially the interestingly leafed variety – the Autumn-tinged oak leaf, lamb's tongue, curly endive, crunchy red radicchio, tender spinach leaves, sorrel, spicy watercress and nasturtium leaves. A few of these leaves add verve to the standard Cos, Iceberg or hothouse lettuce-based salad.

Facts about fats

Too much fat can raise one's cholesterol level and clog up the arteries, ultimately leading to heart problems.

However, a certain amount of fat is needed to help protect the body's vital organs and to provide body heat and energy.

Make a point of eating less fat, especially saturated animal fats, so spread the butter sparingly on your bread and for weight loss use a low-fat spread which contains half the calories found in either butter or margarine.

Dress Up your Salad

With of course, only the very best olive, walnut or hazelnut oil. The first pressings or extra extra Virgin oils that come from France and Italy are best. Olive oil is popular in Mediterranean countries where, it is worth noting, heart disease incidence is very low. Use an equally good quality wine vinegar for your dressing. Some vinegars, like fine Champagnes, are produced only in exceptional years and are at their best when they have some bottle age, perhaps even fifty years. Otherwise, choose a white wine vinegar made from the elegant Chardonnay Champagne grape.

The merest 'pinch'

Too much salt (according to the experts we are all offenders) leads to high blood pressure. Refined salt, like refined flour, is not part of this Diet, but a little Rock or Sea salt is permitted. This contains iodine that stimulates the thyroid gland, which in turn helps the metabolism to function efficiently.

A cause of fatness can be too much salt in the diet, which leads to water retention. By cutting down on salt you could help the pounds diminish too.

However, gourmets and cooks need to use salt sometimes to bring out the flavour of certain foods. In this case, taste before you sprinkle and you may find you don't need any at all. Try flavouring food with alternative herbs and spices. Lemon juice for example, is a good substitute for salt with meat, poultry and fish.

The Salt Balancer

You can balance the sodium (it's the sodium in salt that's bad) with potassium.

Potassium is found in citrus fruits, figs, bananas, watercress, green peppers, meat, fish and grains.

If you are overly fond of salt, eat plenty of watercress with your meals or have a sliced banana, a fruit very high in potassium, with your breakfast cereal.

Your aim is to gradually reduce your salt intake to the merest 'pinch'.

To sin is to take sugar

Apart from ruining your teeth and bringing you out in spots, sugar-rich foods are the ones that can make you ideal casting for Grand Opera. Sugar is not a food as it has no nutritional value. Whenever possible fruit or dried fruit should be substituted for sugar and when you feel in need of a quick energy boost take a handful of grapes or whatever fruit is available.

For that morning bite

In spite of its sugar content, marmalade made from bitter Seville oranges that have had the white pith left on the skin has a 'wake you up' tang, freshens the taste-buds and the acids in the pith clean the teeth more effectively than many a toothpaste. Unfortunately, it is only home-made marmalade that has these dual qualities so buy the best Seville orange marmalade you can find to spread on your wholemeal toast. The Spanish onion has a different effect!

For Gourmets with a Sweet Tooth

Every diet must have its delectation, which need not be its downfall. On this diet it is chocolate, dark, plain and bitter, either thinly sculptured into shapes that act as containers for fruits, mousses, sorbets or parfaits, or on its own.

Be seduced by a super chocolate but not before 9 p.m. Chocolate is an indulgence and you mustn't be tempted until after the evening meal and then by a mint or mocha-flavoured stick or a Champagne truffle (70 calories a fling). The very best chocolates contain over 50% cacao which more than redeems the sinful sugar content because cacao induces a blissful state of utter contentment, a state in which you might find yourself murmuring to yourself, 'I love you, I think you're beautiful'.

Nearly all quality chocolates contain lecithin which is a nutrient derived from the Soya bean. Apart from helping to burn up fats it also keeps the body fats moving so that they don't settle in susceptible areas.

Is it food or an explosive?

You could be forgiven for wondering when the contents on the label lists such items as Crumbs with Colour E102, or antioxidant E30, Gelling Agents E401, Caseinate, Emulsifiers E472b, Fumaric Acid and a stabilizer. Your stomach would need a stabilizer if you were to eat this kind of convenience food.

Much better to keep to recognizable nourishment like fish, oysters and caviar.

Some of the best fish in the world, sole, hake and halibut, come from the cold, North Atlantic waters. Meanwhile, the King of fish, the wild salmon, spends a lot of its life in the rivers, swimming and leaping upstream in an effort to get back to its breeding grounds. This leaping and swimming upstream keeps it slender, giving it more taste and less fat than the salmon reared in peaceful Highland lochs.

Fish is an excellent source of protein, low in saturated fat, besides containing vital minerals like calcium and phosphorous.

Crustaceans

A Champagne Diet would be incomplete without oysters, lobsters and giant-sized Dublin Bay Prawns, alias French Langoustine and Italian Scampi.

An oyster is only five calories and full of rejuvenating protein; besides being a rich source of phosphorous salts, chalk, iron, copper, manganese and a high proportion of iodine, it also contains vitamins A, B1, C and D.

Apart from being a food it is regarded as a beauty treatment, restoring water content to the skin and lessening facial lines and wrinkles, but its greatest claim to fame is that it may be an aphrodisiac.

Lobster meat and deshelled prawns are only thirty calories an ounce of concentrated protein. Protein clings to the ribs which is why small portions go further.

Caviar for glamour

Eggs, whether they come from cod, plaice, sole or any other fish, have exceptional nutritional value, but the most glamorous roe comes from the female sturgeon – caviar. Only seventy-five calories an ounce, it is a perfectly balanced food containing 30% protein, 16% polyunsaturated fish fat and 4% minerals; the rest is water.

Happy Beef

A lot of meat comes from animals which are mass reared. They are injected with hormones to plump them up and since penned cattle are easy prey to illness and disease, they are regularly injected with antibiotics to kill any germs. When we eat meat raised in these conditions we consume hormones and antibiotics retained in the meat's fatty tissues.

You are more likely to avoid this by eating quality meat from animals which have been allowed to graze on pastureland rather than having been cooped up in unhealthy battery conditions.

The best beef is the Scottish Black Angus, or the Charolias from France. In Japan, the prize cattle are particularly well-looked-after, getting a daily hand massage to ensure tender steaks. People are treated with less sensitivity.

Wild venison, hare and rabbit or birds like pheasant and duck which have also missed the hypodermic needle are low on fat because they have been running or flying around and have lots of flavour from grazing on sweet meadow grass and nibbling the tops of herb-flavoured hedges.

The hi-fibrous Bird

Chicken is a particularly good food for slimmers as it is low in fats yet high in protein. Again, you need to avoid battery reared birds that have been raised on cheap fish meal. Look for free-range chickens which have led happy lives strutting and clucking around a farmyard while waiting to be fed their hi-fibre diet of maize, corn and milk.

DO's and DONT's of Dieting

DO: Eat slowly. Champagne slows down your eating speed. In order to pick up your glass you have to put down your knife and fork. This reduces your eating speed to a gentle 'cruising' pace. By thoroughly masticating your food and extracting every nuance of texture and taste you'll find that you need less to satisfy your appetite.

DO: Eat less bread. Use a sharp knife and cut your wholemeal bread in wafer-thin slices.

DO: Use less salt; taste before you sprinkle.

DO: Have skimmed milk in tea or coffee; it has approximately half the fat content of other milks in spite of being just as rich in protein and calcium. You need calcium for bone maintenance.

DON'T: Eat fried foods. When the pan requires greasing use a quality oil instead of butter, or a non-stick pan.

DON'T: Take sugar in tea or coffee: don't even keep any in the house. Keep one pot of the best honey for your breakfast cereal, but try, if possible, to replace the honey with natural fruit sugars which are found in all fresh and dried fruits.

DON'T: Above all else, become a calorie counter, they are such dreary bores. You'll find that by cutting down on fats, sugars especially, white starches and eating smaller portions of food, and eating slowly, your calorie intake will diminish anyway.

4 *How to Follow the Champagne Diet*

'I am drinking stars' exclaimed the monk in rapturous tones as he took his first sip of Champagne.

'Drinking stars' is the lift that a diet needs to drag it away from the grapefruit and lettuce doldrums and make it a success. The reason why so many diets fail is because they are based on the self-denial principle: 'Can't do this', 'Mustn't have that' and similar dull repetitions.

This diet works because it has style and is glamorous besides being slimming and healthy.

When to Drink Champagne and How Much

This might be your first question and who better to answer it than Madame Bollinger who said, 'I drink it when I'm happy and when I'm sad. Sometimes I drink it when I'm alone. When I have company I consider it obligatory. I trifle with it if I'm not hungry and drink it when I am. Otherwise, I never touch it – unless I'm thirsty.'

This pretty well covers all possibilities. However, on the diet restraint is necessary. Aim for around three or four glasses a day, so you may decide to miss a glass at lunchtime preferring to have an early evening apéritif followed by a couple of glasses during dinner and one instead of a liqueur or port at the end. There could be emergency situations, however. For example:

Do You Flag at 11(am)?

Perhaps you are suffering from a shortage of Pink. Colour affects our moods and emotions. Picasso had his 'blue' period, white is spiritual, black sombre, pastel shades soothe, whereas red incites the passions. To view life through 'pink-tinted' spectacles is a philosophical way of seeing things at their rosiest. Looking at pink, especially when it sparkles, is in a glass and called Taittinger Comtes de

Champagne lifts the morale up to Cloud Nine. Strangely enough, golden hued Champagne doesn't have quite that effect in the morning; it must be the colour that counts.

For Those Stressful Moments

Instead of swallowing pills, take your minerals and vitamins the natural way; drink a glass of Champagne.

Pure quality wines contain mineral salts such as potassium, iron, calcium and magnesium, plus water-soluble vitamins C and B complex, according to Dr Maury in his book '*Wine is the Best Medicine*'.

For those days that seem more fateful than others try this Mimosa Cocktail. Whisk a raw egg yolk (protein and lecithin) with freshly squeezed orange juice (vitamin C) and top up with Champagne.

Become a Two-Handed Drinker

As part of the diet don't forget the Champagne Companion. Make it a habit to match each glass of Champagne with a glass and a half of mineral water. There is something very reassuring about having two glasses on the go. Sip the Champagne and swallow the water. If you are in the middle of an animated conversation you are not always aware of what you are drinking anyway. On those occasions reach for the water and save the bubbles for the lull when you can give them your undivided attention.

You are attempting to drink a ratio of approximately 60% water to 40% Champagne, but if it occasionally gets closer to 50% – 50% don't worry. Don't swing into reverse though and drink more Champagne than water.

How Much Weight to Lose

At the onset of your diet you need to decide how much weight you want to lose. As a general guideline, if you want to lose less than two stone cut down to between 1,300 and 1,500 calories a day. Don't rush, however, and try to lose two stone in two weeks. It probably took you months, even years, to collect the surplus so don't try or expect to be unencumbered in a fortnight.

Aim to lose eight to twelve pounds in four weeks. It's a happy diet, so if you have to stay with it for another four to eight weeks it will not be a hardship.

For Extra Weight Loss

If after a week or so, the pounds won't move cut your calories to 900 to 1,000 a day for two or three days.

Indulge your whims

If the menu is very tempting, don't resist, eat and enjoy yourself (within reason), for tomorrow is another day when you *can* take care of the previous day's excesses. Perhaps you overdid it by 500 calories; that's all right, the balance can be adjusted during the forthcoming week. It's not your daily but your overall weekly intake that counts. This means you can eat and drink according to the social occasion and your lifestyle. For example, you had a marvellous seven-course banquet (small taste-provoking portions, naturally); the next morning you are not so hungry, so choose the low-calorie Slimmer's Special, followed at lunchtime with a small fish delicacy. By the evening you may be getting your appetite back so dine at home and prepare one of the special Slender Gourmet dinners.

The diet consists of three meals a day, breakfast, lunch and dinner. No snacks between meals.

A Prelude to the Day

Breakfast is important to start afresh and put the best fork forward. You can choose from one of three breakfasts depending on how hungry you feel, what you had to eat the previous evening and what your plans are for the day ahead.

The traditional bacon and eggs, white toast and sugary sweet marmalade washed down with coffee is OUT. It is too high in foods that form acids in the body. Over-acidity can lead to all sorts of minor and major complaints like indigestion, insatiable appetite, cellulitis and arthritis. Any of these conditions could turn you into a Failed Slender Gourmet and hobbling to your favourite bar stool is not the Champagne image.

Every morning it is important to re-establish the body's acid/alkaline balance. A healthy body needs to maintain a ratio of approximately 75% alkaline to 25% acid.

The following three breakfasts take care of this.

If you wake up feeling 'peckish' or have a long day ahead with the possibility of only a light lunch, then the Slender Gourmet Health Bowl is nourishing. It lines the stomach and keeps the hunger pangs at bay.

Breakfast No. 1 *The Slender Gourmet Health Bowl*

Make a mix from both the acid- and alkaline-forming foods on this list. Aim for three parts alkaline to one part acid.

Alkaline-forming foods	cals	Acid-forming foods	cals
½ carton natural yoghurt	30	Grains and cereals.	
Fresh or dried fruit:		2 tbsp. crunchy Muesli	
1 oz. berries	8	including a sprinkling of	
½ apple	7	seeds like sunflower,	
small peach or pear	30	pumpkin, sesame	200
5 dried apricots or hunzas	50		
(soaked overnight)		Tsp. honey (optional)	30

Oh, that this too too solid flesh would melt ... Hamlet didn't know, but if you want to help the body burn up surplus fats, sprinkle Lecithin granules over your Muesli. Remember what I said about Lecithin in the chapter on Healthy Eating.

Breakfast No. 2 *The Continental*

Presentation is everything. A large tray covered with a white linen cloth on which reposes a glass of chilled, freshly squeezed (only minutes before) orange juice, thinly sliced wholemeal toast aerating in a silver toast rack, and a jar of marmalade made from Seville oranges. This should be accompanied by a pot of China tea (less caffeine content than Indian) – either a Lapsang Souchong which has delicate, smoky overtones or Green Gunpowder which, far from being explosive, is practically caffeine free. If you prefer coffee with your breakfast choose a de-caffeinated variety.

A perfect flower in a vase provides food for the soul, while a copy of *The Times* provides something for the brain. Definitely a breakfast to linger over.

Breakfast No. 3 *The Slimmer's Special*

If you had a rather splendid meal the previous evening, you might need to economize on your calories, so half a pink grapefruit (30 calories) and a cup of Mint tea made from fresh mint leaves.

A Little Midday Sustenance

Lunch should be light, nutritious and sustaining. Oysters, caviar, giant prawns, lobster, crab, smoked salmon are all low-calorie, high-protein foods. Eaten with a green salad or vegetables they provide all the nutrition your body needs to carry you over until the dinner gong.

A simple lunch at home might be:

2 or 3 giant prawns (if you are not too squeamish do suck the prawn's head, it's tasty and rich in minerals.)
2 or 3 little mouth-size quail's eggs.
Unlimited sprigs of watercress, lemon juice and pepper.
2 wafer-thin slices of wholemeal bread covered with the merest scrape of butter.
Fruit in season or a slice of melon.

The Moon Rises

The day builds up to the evening meal when there is time to sit down, either at home or in a restaurant, so why not make it the entire evening's entertainment?

5 *Following the Champagne Diet at Home*

A Chef's Lament

'My poor body, heavy with the residue of so many rich and delectable sauces, was so well covered that it weighed me to the ground and around my waist the centimetres crept, covering a considerable distance,' lamented Michael Guérard, a very fat Chef. Deciding to do something about his weight problem, he went to a Health Farm, where he reported receiving 'a sharp blow in the taste buds'. After eating what seemed like endless acres of undressed lettuce leaves and grated carrots, he emerged many kilos lighter but bordering on despair, 'unable' he said 'to feel the vibrations that made his eye, nose, palate and touch sing when a really successful dish appeared'. He felt isolated, cut off, surrounded by a closing wall of frustration. Out of this despair developed a resolve to create a new style of cooking which would appeal to people who love to eat but want to lose weight.

He experimented with new ways of cooking using very little fat and no flour or sugar and achieved a much lighter style of cuisine which he called Cuisine Minceur.

Cuisine Minceur was the first of the gourmet-style, healthy-eating cuisines which appealed to overweight gourmands.

This was followed by Nouvelle Cuisine which specialised in small portions. The visual effects were overly contrived, you eat more with your eyes than with your palate. As most diners left the table feeling depleted in their stomachs as well as their pockets this in turn was replaced by Anton Mosimann's Cuisine Naturelle. This famous Chef formerly of The Dorchester, opened his own exclusive Belgravia Dining Club called 'Mosimann's' where he has become well known for creating light, yet satisfying, cuisine keeping the use of salt, fats, flour and artificial sugars to a minimum.

Bruno Lebout, Chef at The Inn on the Park, made a move away from this concept with his Cuisine Terrior. Back to the earth cooking, Pigs Trotters, Skate, Oxtail, sometimes mixing the simple with the exotic such as Jellied Eel with a Cauliflower mousse topped with Caviar.

More and more Chefs and diners are turning towards the new Cuisine de Vie. Originating in the famous Health Spas in Switzerland it emphasises minimal use of animal fats, artificial sugars and sodium.

In the days of haute cuisine Chefs were traditionally rotund but then they were cooking rich, heavy seven-course meals for diners who often had, and were proud of, gargantuan girths.

Today, everyone is health-conscious and realises that they should eat well-balanced nutritional meals full of the best and freshest produce available.

We are what we eat, and the Cuisine of Life, helps us to be healthier, more energetic and beautiful, and consequently feeling and looking younger.

Apart from eating for health and enjoyment it is also necessary to exercise in order to keep the body purring over like a Rolls-Royce engine, lithesome and streamlined.

I asked the Chefs in this book what they did to keep fit. The answers were interesting.

David Doricott of 'Truffles' at The Portman is a Piste enthusiast executing nifty turns on the mountain slopes.

Giovanni, their Restaurant Manager, is a Judo black belt. However, he does not throw his weight about in the Restaurant.

Colin Button at 'Celebrities' does a brisk forty-minute walk from Victoria Station through St James's Park, to the Hampshire Hotel in Leicester Square, morning and evening, and flexi knee bends when opening the oven.

Peter Kromberg at 'Le Soufflé' is a formidable Squash player and gardening addict.

Avner Samuel from The Churchill Hotel used to clock up 400 miles a week on his bicycle; now it's more like a few laps around the neighbouring Serpentine. He sings when he is happy, which is when he cooks, exercising his lungs by bursting into song in French, Hebrew or English.

Michael Coaker of 'Le Chateau' 'goes for the burn' on the Exercise Bicycle at The Mayfair's Health Club.

Gary, the Patissiere Chef, spends two hours every evening working with weights, preparing himself for 'Mr Universe Muscle Man' Competitions.

John Bertram is a family man who, rain or shine, chases around the tennis court with his four children every Sunday morning.

Adam Palmer, Head Chef at Champneys, occasionally drops out of the sky, attached to a parachute; a good way of aerating the lungs.

To top up their fitness, Chefs from the exclusive 'Club Nine' visit Champneys at Tring. Just recently six of them spent five days exercising, relaxing and eating Adam Palmer's calorie conscious cuisine.

If you feel like being venturesome in the kitchen try out some of their Recipes, but do remember the golden rule ...

If you want to lose weight, eat less and exercise more.

To gain weight, the reverse applies.

Once you are the weight and shape you want to be, then Calories In have to equal Calories Out.

All the recipes serve four people, apart from the marvellous Chocolate and Cinnamon Parfait which serves eight.

Ham and Parsley Terrine

A 200 g (8 oz) slipper of bacon (soaked in cold water for 24 hours)
60 g (2 oz) chopped washed parsley
4 leaves gelatine
1 carrot
1 onion
1 leek
1 stick celery

Soak gelatine and leave to stand.
Poach the bacon with the vegetables for 20 minutes in just enough water to cover.
Remove the meat and flake it.
Strain the stock and add the gelatine to make 300ml (½ pint) liquid.
Combine the bacon and parsley and place in a small terrine.
Fill with the stock and refrigerate for two hours.

Turn out and serve as an hors d'oeuvre with a red cabbage coleslaw.

Colin Button, Chef de Cuisine at The Hampshire Hotel

Tortilla Soup

4 large red tomatoes
2 large onions
1 large clove garlic
1200 ml (1 qt) chicken stock
1 tsp cumin
1 tsp ground chilli pepper
1 small bunch of coriander
30 ml (1 fl. oz) corn oil
3 corn tortillas
2 tbs tomato purée
a little salt

Garnish
½ avocado, diced
½ breast of chicken (poached and diced)
2 corn tortilla (cut into strips)
90 g (3 oz) red leicester cheese (grated)

Purée the onion and tomato.
In stock pot, put corn oil, garlic (cut in halves), and 3 corn tortillas. Sauté until golden brown.
Add purée to the stock pot and saute for two minutes. Add chicken and spices to stock and cook for 45 minutes.
Add salt to taste and strain through a fine strainer.
In centre of soup plate, place corn tortilla strips, diced avocado, and poached and diced chicken with red leicester. Pour tortilla soup on top and serve hot.

Avner Samuel, Chef de Cuisine at The Churchill Hotel

Breast of Chicken Stuffed with Leeks and Olives and served with Light Tomato Vinaigrette

4 100 g (4 oz) chicken breasts
100 g (4 oz) leeks
12 pitted black olives
salt and black pepper
500 ml (16 fl. oz) chicken stock

Vinaigrette
4 medium-sized tomatoes
2 tsp soya oil
2 tsp white wine vinegar
½ tsp (pinch) Canderel sweetener
salt and black pepper
4 leaves fresh basil

Heat oven to 400°F/200°C/Gas 6.
Remove skin and wing bones from the breasts. Cut pockets in the breast 3″ long and 1½″ wide.
Shred the leeks into fine strips and mix well with the finely diced olives.
Season each chicken breast inside the cavity, and stuff with leek mixture.
Reshape chicken breasts and place in an earthenware dish.
Bring chicken stock to the boil and pour over breasts, making sure they are completely covered.
Cook in a preheated oven for twenty minutes.

Vinaigrette
Purée tomatoes in a food processor.
Add all the ingredients.
When all the ingredients are emulsified, strain into a bowl and chill in the refrigerator.

To serve: arrange the chicken on a plate. Pour over the vinaigrette and garnish.

Adam Palmer, Head Chef at Champneys Health Club at Tring

Cod Steak 'Oriental'

4 180 g (6 oz) cod steaks
100 g (4 oz) wheat germ
100 g (4 oz) beansprouts
100 g (4 oz) snow peas, cut in small pieces
100 g (4 oz) carrots, cut in slices
60 g (2 oz) radishes, cut in slices
1 lemon
1½ tbsp sesame oil
1½ tbsp soya sauce
salt, pepper

Heat oil in a frying pan.
Season steaks with lemon juice, salt and pepper.
Fry steaks 3 minutes each side (depending on size). Remove from pan and keep hot.
Mix vegetables and stir fry them quickly in the same pan. Add soya sauce and seasoning.
Serve immediately to ensure vegetables are crisp.
Serve with some basmati rice.

David Doricott, Chef de Cuisine at The Portman Hotel

Champagne Risotto

60 g (2 oz) onion, chopped
375 g (12 oz) Vialone or Arborio rice
150 ml (¼ pt) Champagne
300 ml (½ pt) chicken stock
90 g (3 oz) Parmesan cheese, grated

Seafood for the Risotto
4 scampi, cubed
4 large shrimp, cubed
4 fillets of sole, cubed
200 g (8 oz) turbot or brill, cubed
4 Coquilles St Jacques
8 fresh tomatoes, skinned, cubed and dried

1 tbsp Cognac
a dab of butter
a small shallot, finely diced
a little parsley, basil and dill, chopped
salt and pepper

Sauté the onions in the sunflower oil. Add the rice and champagne.
Cook the rice slowly for 20 minutes, gradually adding the chicken stock. When cooked, add the Parmesan cheese.
Melt the butter and in it cook the onions. Then add all the fish and sauté it with the Cognac.
Add the tomatoes and cook for a few minutes.
Add all the herbs.
At the last moment, add the seafood to the Risotto and serve.

John Bertram, Chef de Cuisine at Scotts Restaurant

Chartreuse de Perdrix

2 wild grey-legged partridges or pheasants
6–10 kg (3–5 lb) Savoy cabbage
90 g (3 oz) foie gras
2 garlic sausages
300 ml (½ pt) patridge juice
150 ml (1 gill) brandy
150 ml (1 gill) Madeira
a little vegetable oil

Heat oven to 400°F/200°C/Gas 6.
Sauté the partridges for about 4-5 minutes, and then flambé with brandy and Madeira.
Blanch the cabbage.
Prepare round china dishes. Line the sides of the terrines with the blanched Savoy cabbage, then add the partridges and the sausages.
Next add a layer of braised cabbage and some cubes of foie gras. Add the partridge juice between each layer.
Arrange cabbage leaves over the top to close it up.
Cook for approximately 1½ hours.
Garnish with *Pommes Vapeurs*, sausages and partridge juice montée au foie gras (foie gras passed through a sieve and mixed with partridge juice).

Peter Kromberg, Maitre Chef de Cuisine at the Hotel Inter-Continental

King Prawns Japanese Style

8 king prawns
20 ml (½ fl. oz) sesame oil
4 cucumber fan
5 g (pinch) red and green seaweed
4 lemon wedges
20 g (½ oz) poppy seeds

Marinade (to make 1.2 litres (2 pt))
600 ml (1 pt) sesame oil
600 ml (1 pt) mirin
2 bay leaves
4 parsley sprigs
1 sprig of thyme
a squeeze of lime juice
salt and white pepper
5 g (pinch) poppy seeds

Sashima sauce (to make 910 ml (1¾ pt))
150 ml (¼ pt) sake
150 ml (¼ pt) mirin
375 ml (¾ pt) dark soy sauce
150 ml (¼ pt) tamarin
85 ml (3 fl. oz) bonito flakes
3 small pieces of kelp

To make the marinade, mix all the ingredients together, and measure off 40 ml (1 fl. oz) for use in this recipe.
To make the sashima sauce, heat the sake and mirin in a pan, flame and reduce by half. Add the soy sauce and tamarin, bring to the boil and reduce slightly. Remove from heat, and add the bonito flakes and kelp. Leave to cool and strain. Measure off 40 ml (1 fl. oz) for use in this recipe.
Marinade the king prawns for 60 minutes, then blanch them in the marinade.
Remove the shell and outer casing, leaving the tail section on. Split each prawn in two, keeping them attached by the tail and remove entrails. Brush with oil and sprinkle with poppy seeds.
Pour a little of the sashima sauce on each plate. Arrange 2 prawns on each plate and decorate with cucumber fan, seaweed and lemon wedge.

Chef Anton Mosimann for British Airways, Concorde

Mousse de Yaourt aux Fraises et Parfume a l'Orange

100 ml (4 fl. oz) fromage frais
4 leaves gelatine
200 ml (8 fl. oz) plain yoghurt
3 oranges
6–8 strawberries, diced
60 g (2 oz) icing sugar

Grate the orange zest and squeeze out the juice. Put it into a saucepan, bring to the boil and reduce by half, then take off the heat.
Soak the gelatine. Squeeze out excess water and add to the orange juice.
Mix yoghurt, fromage frais and icing sugar together. Strain the orange juice and mix it into the yoghurt and fromage frais mix.
Finally add the diced strawberries to the mix, and pour into a long mould, preferably a terrine.

To serve: When the mousse is set, warm the mould by placing it into some warm water to release the mousse and turn it out.
Slice the mousse into four portions with a serrated knife or, even better, an electric carving-knife.
Garnish to your liking and serve.

Chef's notes:
Honey can be used in place of icing sugar.
Make sure the mousse does not become too cold once you have added the gelatine or the mousse will set before you have added the strawberries.

Michael Coaker, Chef de Cuisine at the May Fair Hotel

Chocolate and Cinnamon Parfait with Espresso Sauce

200 g (8 oz) bitter chocolate
150 g (5 oz) butter
5 egg yolks
7 egg whites
30 g (1 oz) icing sugar
Cinnamon to taste

Sauce
600 ml (1 pt) milk
3 espresso measures of coffee
4–5 egg yolks
60 g (2 oz) castor sugar

Melt the butter and chocolate over a pan of hot water. Whilst the chocolate is still warm, add the yolks and mix thoroughly.
Whisk the egg whites until they form soft peaks and add the icing sugar.
Fold into the chocolate mixture and add ground cinnamon to taste.
Pour parfait into a clingfilm-lined mould and freeze overnight.

For the sauce: Mix the milk and coffee together and bring to the boil.
Whisk the egg yolks and castor sugar together until smooth and creamy and pour on to the milk. Cook gently over a low heat until the sauce thickens, taking care not to allow the sauce to boil.
Pass through a thin chinois and allow to cool.

To assemble: Turn out the parfait. With a sharp knife dipped in warm water, cut slices of parfait and arrange on eight plates.
Pour the coffee sauce around, and sprinkle with a little cinnamon.

Robert Ridley, Chef at The Halcyon Hotel

Dining at Home

Eating at home should be just as enjoyable as dining out. Invite a friend to dinner, set the scene, a candlelit table with the Champagne cooling in an ice bucket (filled with ice cubes and water). Everything should sparkle, the Champagne, the *pièce de resistance*, the conversation and the glassware. To do justice to Champagne the choice of glass is important; it should show off the colour and bubbles to best advantage. Make sure that you like the weight and feel of the glass in your hand, apart from its decorative appearance on the table.

Do you have a languishing mousse?

Choose the narrow flute or tall tulip rather than the open saucer type glass whose shape encourages the bubbles to dissipate. There is nothing more irksome than having repeatedly to top up your glass from the bottle in an effort to revive a languishing mousse.

Professor Claus Riedel, one of the great glassmakers, may have come up with the answer. After years of research he has evolved a technique whereby the glass not only holds the bubbles for a longer period of time but keeps them active as they leave the glass to settle on the tastebuds of the tongue, filling, as the Professor says 'our mouth with a festive tingling'.

I have my own way of coping with diminishing bubbles, which you may like to try, but you will need …

A Gentleman with a half carat Diamond Tie-Pin

Sometimes hard to come by, but a diamond on the end of a long pin allows him to scratch criss-cross lines inside the glass, at the base. This roughening of the surface encourages the bubbles to spiral upwards in a continuous well controlled slender column.

How to keep the Bubbles in the Bottle

The cork has been extracted. In the absence of a Champagne clamp, how can you prevent the wine going flat during the course of the evening? A silver teaspoon placed in the neck of the bottle will ensure the spontaneity of your mousse until the very last drop.

Advice from Voltaire

Voltaire, slender as a wand, wrote immortal prose. He himself lived to be a creditable, if not respectable, eighty-four. Perhaps his best advice, applicable to Slender Gourmets, was at the end of *Candide* when he reminded us to 'cultivate our garden'. Plant plenty of vegetables. Eat lots of green salads. Make sure that your salad bowl is as distinguished as your glassware and Champagne bucket. Choose a large roomy one, perhaps hand-carved out of an interestingly marked rich wood like olive. It should be spacious so that when you toss the contents each leaf is covered with a fine coat of dressing.

goes to:-

~ London ~

le Souffle
Celebrities
The Halcyon

Scotts
Truffles
The Restaurant at the Churchill

le Chateau
Overtons

~ New York ~

le Cirque
Windows on the World

QE2
Concorde

The Jockey Club
The Four Seasons

6 Following the Champagne Diet – Dining Out

What Makes a Restaurant Great

The success of a restaurant depends on the policy of the Management, not to cut corners but to shop in the world markets daily and buy only the very best and freshest of ingredients.

The value of a Chef and staff is also of paramount importance as was appreciated only too well by the French aristocrats during the Revolution when they fled their country making sure that the most important members of their household escaped with them. Irrespective of their nearest and dearest it was often the Chef and the Sous Chef who escaped with the Marquis and settled in Soho where they opened restaurants.

Not only the ability but the philosophy of the Chef is vital to the success of a restaurant.

'If the Chef has not got the right attitude to cooking, the dish will be a failure – the soufflé will not rise.' So said Michael Quinn, ex-Chef of The Ritz.

It is important to visit restaurants that employ talented creative Chefs who mastermind the menus. Besides wanting to create great dishes, they must also be aware of food values, of health and diet, and who are open to new ideas and ways of cooking.

Traditional haute cuisine can be rich and heavy, sometimes providing a way for parsimonious cooks to save money by disguising inferior cuts of meat with thick, floury sauces. A lighter, simpler style of cooking is now favoured relying on the best ingredients which are enhanced (not disguised) with light sauces made by a reduction of mingled juices, wines and herbs. Lean cuts of meat are chosen, less butter and cream is used and subtler combinations of flavours, textures, aromas and colours are the rule, with a greater use of herbs and exotic fruits.

Pastry, puddings and flour-based dishes are kept to an absolute minimum and when served are in miniature sizes. The only pastry permitted is 'puff' – the air being calorie-free.

A Chef cooks for the personal needs of the diner. If the diner is an aspiring Slender Gourmet and not a fat glutton, then he will compose dishes with this image in mind.

The cook must prepare food with love and care; if he cooks carelessly, with indifference and a chip on the shoulder, then the dish will reflect his attitude.

How often have you eaten out and been disappointed by the quality of the food? How often, for example, much to the distress of yourself and your guests, has the allegorical soufflé fallen flat on its face? To avoid this happening, and to help you stay with your Diet, I am listing some Restaurants that have won The Slender Gourmet Award for Joie de Vivre Cuisine.

Joie de Vivre Cuisine

It's surprising how quickly a delicious meal and a few flutes of Champagne lifts me out of the doldrums. So much so in fact that I decided to create a Slender Gourmet Award for those Chefs whose cooking meets this criterion.

My advice to dieters is, don't become too calorie-dominated for it can put a dampener on your joie. Instead become taste-conscious and health-orientated, choosing the best and freshest produce wherever possible. If you want to lose weight follow the Do's and Don'ts for Dieters on pages 24 and 25.

Eating and drinking involves the senses of sight, smell and taste which develop our critical faculties and appreciation of the finer things in life. Food and wine is the perfect accompaniment to the Arts, especially the art of good conversation, of flirtatious repartee and the priceless pleasure of sharing food and wine with friends, companions and loved ones. It creates the ambience for merriment, laughter, occasionally the profound thought and the odd 'bon mot'.

Happily eating occurs every day so the pleasure can be constantly renewed.

Bon Appetit.

Scotts Caviar and Oyster Bar, Mount Street, W.1.

Although adjoining the famous Scotts Restaurant, the Caviar and Oyster Bar has its own private entrance and individual atmosphere.

Captains of Industry in a hurry can sit at the Oyster Bar and scan a conveniently placed copy of the *Financial Times* as they enjoy half a dozen No. 1s with a cool glass of Chablis.

Those with more leisure can dine at tables, sitting on comfortable banquettes or chairs, and be tempted by John Bertram's sea specialities – *Sole à la Scotts*, Dover sole fillets poached in white wine and adorned with scallops, langoustines and asparagus; Lobster Newburg, cooked in Champagne; or a Dressed Crab and salad. Whilst eating your 'dressed' Crab take a look at the colourful set of wall paintings to know what an 'undressed' Crab is 'almost wearing', showing amongst other crustaceans, a curvaceous Crab vamp in sexy underwear with of course, 6 feelers and 2 claws.

The Inplace for Caviar Eaters.

The 'Sharing' Bar, which runs diagonally across the centre of the room seating four either side and one at each end, exudes caviar charisma.

Frequent visitors to Scotts have their image captured by cartoonist Donald Green and then affixed to a place mat. When you sit down an element of anticipation exists as you wonder if one of them might turn up, and you will find yourself sitting next to a close friend or relative of the Kerman family who own Scotts, TV comedian David Ireland, the famous film director of *Henry V*, Stephen Evans, or you might find yourself sharing your caviar adornments with JR or other members of the Dallas Soap Opera who have the Caviar Compulsion.

Caviar to Some People ...

The first time I had those moist greyish eggs was in the Veranda Grill on the Queens. A life-sized Swan, carved from a block of glittering ice, was wheeled to my side and there, buried deep in crushed ice, lay a stone pot containing a myriad of firm, plump Mallesol eggs.

On another occasion I was being entertained by a love-sick White Russian, who accompanied the Beluga eggs with songs sung in a sad, deep base that turned to grief on presentation of the bill.

You can choose from three top Caviars, Beluga, Oscietra and Sevruga. The Beluga eggs are the largest, dark greyish black with a dreamy, creamy flavour.

The Golden Oscietra have a bright colour and are graded large with a slightly nutty, fresh sweet taste.

The Sevruga eggs are the smallest, coming from the smallest Sturgeon, they are very dark grey almost black and tastefully tangy to the palate.

Living the Magical Moment

Chopped eggs and onions are sometimes requested to accompany the Caviar, but are only served with great reluctance at Scotts. Purists disapprove of these adornments because they disguise the delicate flavour of the roe. Toast points only are permitted; even a slice of lemon is suspect.

According to Mr Petrossian, owner of a well-known New York Caviar Bar, six or seven eggs should be trowelled directly on to the tongue from a gold-tipped

Caviar, to some people

palette (silver is unacceptable), kept in the mouth for a second, then rolled on the tongue until the eggs burst against the palate, releasing their full flavour. Above all, he recommends that you don't talk or allow any external influences to detract your attention from the 'eggs-in-the-mouth moment'.

Eva Zarach of the firm Aneva Limited, Caviar suppliers, prefers a palette made from horn or bone. I was taught to put a few eggs on the back of the hand, rather like taking snuff, sniffing first, then eating and afterwards sniffing the skin again to relive the scent of the sea.

If you plan to eat Caviar on a regular basis it might be as well to travel with your own palette, failing which, scooping with your little finger is fun.

How to Stretch your Caviar

A little Caviar has to go a long way, Scotts offers a choice of four stretching methods.

Your fifty grams of Caviar could be served with Blinis Crême Blanche, Russian Buckwheat pancakes with sour cream. Caviar Tartar, thin slices of toast and steak tartar. Tsar Nicholas (Nicky Kerman's favourite), sliced steamed potatoes, smoked salmon and sour cream. Blinis à la Scotts, Russian Buckwheat pancakes, smoked salmon and sour cream.

Practise a little Economy

Fifty grams of Oscietra (a generous portion) will cost £39 and Beluga is more than double this. Since Caviar is the most luxurious food in the World, it has been described as one of Life's Grand Unaffordables, why not practise a small economy? Drink the Slimmer's Champagne, the Laurent Perrier's Ultra Brut or Charles Heidsieck's Brut Sauvage, which contain HALF THE CALORIES of any other Champagne.

Don't forget your two glasses of mineral water which are, of course, calorie-free.

'Truffles' at The Portman Inter-Continental Hotel, Portman Square

The five-star restaurant in The Portman Hotel is named after one of the most exotic foods known to Man. Likened to black diamonds, and with an elusive perfume that gourmets find irresistible, the Truffle is regarded as a highly prized flavour and adornment to many dishes.

It is only to be expected that a restaurant called 'Truffles' should aspire to gastronomical pinnacles and that its cuisine should be liberally sprinkled with black truffles from Périgord and, occasionally, white ones from Elba. Both varieties are difficult to find as they lie buried anywhere between three inches and three feet below ground. The heavenly scent that attracts gourmets also attracts truffle hounds and passionate pigs who uncover the fungi with their snouts, and then reluctantly relinquish them to their masters who acquire vast sums for these edible rarities in the world markets.

Truffles is on the first floor overlooking Portman Square. At night, the view from the windows is very pretty with street lamplights shining against the trees. A little imagination coupled with Champagne would make it easy to drift back to another world of horse-drawn carriages and elegant society hostesses who lived in the neighbouring great houses designed by Robert Adam and who entertained the Wits, Intellectuals and dashing Cavalry Officers of the day. The Earl of Cardigan would have been one whose claim to fame, apart from the woolly jacket, was the disastrous Charge of the Light Brigade.

The restaurant is inviting with its dark wood panels inset with woven tapestries and glass which act as discreet table dividers. Pink linen banded with white sets of sparkling glasses and bone china. Subdued lights, flickering candles, large bowls of soft pink roses and carnations, and quietly moving waiters immaculately clad in black and white add to the three-colour tonal palate, creating an air of warm enticement with formal overtones.

At night the resident pianists play a repertoire of classical music, not overly intrusive but sufficiently individual to be charming.

Lunch with the Chef

This can mean either being entertained in the Chef's private dining-room cum office, situated in the kitchens where he can view the activity of Chefs, Sous-Chefs, Saucieries and Patissiers, or in the Restaurant, which was the case when I had lunch with Dee Cayhill and David Doricott, who looked slender and tailor-turned in designer Whites but minus his Toque.

A great restaurant always serves the best and freshest products, ranging from small things like a diversity of home-baked warm breads to the House Champagne. If I am offered a BOB (Buyer's Own Brand) instead of a Grande Marque a seed of apprehension is sown. The House Champagne was Laurent Perrier so I relaxed, especially as it was served in a slender flute with a long elegant stem.

Truffles Tantalize …

David's choice of starter was excellent, Calves' sweetbreads arranged in a circle on top of mixed salad leaves with sprouting wheat germ interlaced with slivers of truffles, dressed with a balsamic vinaigrette flavoured with truffle juice. The truffles stimulated the gastric juices in preparation for the entrée which was Monkfish sealed in a pepper crust, fan-sliced on a bed of fine dauphine potatoes embellished with a sauce made from fish juices, crême frais, thin strands of smoked salmon, Sevruga caviar, chervil, and, an inspirational soupçon of Champagne.

The test of a great Chef lies in his sauces, this sauce deliciously complimented the Monkfish. It is a slimmer's dish being high in protein (6 to 8 oz), protein clings to the ribs, creating a feeling of saturation which lasts and helps prevent those fattening 'nibbles between meals'.

For Meat Lovers

The Tenderloin of Scottish Beef layered with a mousseline of celery and truffles on a Fleurie wine sauce would be my recommendation. The distinctive flavour of the Gamay grape comes through quite strongly and blends together the other elements in the dish.

Truffle portions are generous. They are always on the Menu, though the harvest is only between November and February. David does not use the canned or bottled variety. They are flown in fresh then sliced or diced, vacuum packed and frozen for use throughout the year. Not forgetting, of course, the Truffle juice which is extracted from both Truffle peelings and the occasional damaged one.

When Wilderness is Paradise

A great delicacy at £52 a starter is a whole Truffle served in puff pastry. To paraphrase Omar Khayam, 'a glass of Krug, a Truffle en Croute and the Wilderness of Life is Paradise enow ...'

Alternatively, savour Truffle Soup covered with a lid of puff pastry, the perfumed aromas seep into the puff which, of course, is eaten instead of bread.

Alternatively again, one can indulge quite magnificently in three courses for under £20.

A Symphony of Cheeses

When confronted with a superb Cheese Board I leave the choice to the Maître d'Hôtel and ask him to please create for me a 'Symphony of Cheeses'. He will, of course, start with the lightest and mildest, perhaps a Chèvre working up to a firm Cow's milk, then on to a creamy rich Brie or Boursault, wherever possible choosing unpasteurized Cheeses, finishing with the strongest and most pungent, a blue-veined Stilton or Roquefort. Biscuits rather than bread and a handful of grapes are especially good with the blue.

A Cheese course is important as the acids and enzymes in Cheese aid the digestion and absorption of protein. Protein keeps one beautiful as it rebuilds and nourishes the body cells and connecting tissues.

Trifle with a Truffle

The Dessert Trolley provides a taste of sweetness without cloying and summarises the harmonious structure of the entire meal.

Torn between a Vanilla Bavarois with exotic fruits or a Roulade of two chocolates with a bitter chocolate sauce laced with Grande Marnier, I decided on the former in order to save myself for the temptation which I knew would appear with coffee.

The pleasure of Wining and Dining can be prolonged by lingering over coffee and petit fours, and what else could it be at Truffles but a Chocolate Champagne Truffle. Just one (or two) to melt lovingly and lingeringly in the mouth.

Apart from the à la Carte, a three-course Lunch is £19.50 and a five-course Dinner £30.

The Churchill Hotel in Portman Square

This offers two exemplary Wining and Dining Venues.

The Churchill Bar

Modelled on a Gentleman's Club this spacious room is eminently comfortable without being staid or stuffy. Warm wood panels, the colour of Autumn chestnuts, line the walls and the Cocktail Bar, which twinkles with shining glasses and spherical crystal ice buckets (just waiting for the bottle). You can sit high on a large leather-studded bar stool or sink into the embracing depths of either a receptive armchair or roomy Chesterfield sofa. This country house library atmosphere, reminiscent of Sir Winston's country seat at Chartwell, would have pleased the great man. Family prints and portraits of Winston Churchill's ancestors adorn the walls. His favourite Champagne, Pol Roger, is served at the Bar.

'I cannot live without Champagne' was his War cry, 'In Victory I deserve it; in defeat I need it'. A sentiment we all echo. Lbs in weight and pounds in sterling fluctuate with the vagaries of life so we are constantly in need of either celebrating or commiserating.

Rocked to Sleep in a Jeroboam

Champagne is much more than just a drink; it is a lifestyle and a way of philosophizing about life. Some people are borne with a 'bubble' in their genes – as Christian Pol Roger remarked, 'I was conceived during a Methuselah (this size holds the equivalent of 8 bottles) and cradled to sleep in half a Jeroboam' (A full Jeroboam holds 4 bottles).

Bubbles and Bangers

As you sip your flute of Pol Roger relax, ruminate, and study the Bar Menu – it is the best value in London. Competitive to pub prices, yes, but quality wise, no, it is far far superior. Their steak, kidney and mushroom pie topped with light, home-made pastry is scrumptious and comes straight from the hotel kitchen (it is not the pre-cooked devitalized food flashed through a microwave, characteristic of many pubs today). The man-size portion flanked with fresh broccoli heads is priced at £4.50. As an alternative, how about a glass of 'bub' with Bangers and Mash, also on the Menu, and excellent value at £3.75.

'The Restaurant' at The Churchill

Walking across gleaming marble floors interlaced with herringbone oak to your table, you cannot but marvel at the opulent decor of this Restaurant. Panelled walls and ceiling inset with small unobtrusive lights illuminate the restaurant scene below. Diners, waiters, romanesque-style urns filled with a rich abundance of fresh fruit, wall-to-ceiling glass-and-mirrored columns separate generously sized tables and reflect the stunning steel sculpture by David Annersley which stands by the Long Bar. The walls are ablaze with the strong colours of contemporary pictures painted by major British artists. The contrast of opposites, energy, modernity, vibrancy combined with controlled classicism creates an excitement which, as I found out, is only matched by the Cuisine.

All the Way from Texas

I had lunch with Olivia Hetherington, Director of Marketing, and The Restaurant's new Chef, Avner Samuel, who had been head-hunted and lassoed from the legendary five-star 'Mansion on Turtle Creek' in Dallas where he created the great new South-west Culinary Style. Since he had achieved so much for Texas, I wondered what he would bring to the contemporary British style of eating.

Full of lively energy and enthusiasm his message was intriguing – drawing on the World's markets of rich exotic fruits, vegetables, herbs, spices and as much home produce as possible, especially meats, game, fish and poultry, he creates original taste sensations, vibrant marriages often between opposites – perhaps Quail and Crab – a successful merging of Regional, Mexican, Texan, Indian, Vietnamese, Chinese, Latin-American cuisines. An ethnic mix which epitomizes today's Cosmopolitan Britain.

Homemade Fettuccine with Sauteed Sea Scallops and Asparagus Spears was an excellent starter. The Sea Scallops were particularly succulent as they had been harvested manually by divers, and not by the more economical 'dredging' method which leaves the scallop with a gritty texture. Judicious buying at the markets is one of the hallmarks of a great kitchen.

The Soup of the Day might be Tortilla, a spicy hot soup from Mexico. Corn tortillas, poached chicken breast, diced red leicester and avocado are the firm constituents on which is poured a liquid made from corn, tomato and onion purée, chicken stock flavoured with garlic and Mexican herbs.

A Marriage of Opposites

An appetizer combining the 'noble' with the 'crass' was Foie Gras and potatoes, but Avner's interpretation was quite out of the ordinary. Three potatoes had been shaped into pyramids and coloured, one black with squid ink, another with saffron to make it orange and the third with beet juice which turned it red. Another potato had been shredded and pan fried providing a crispy brown base for a warm slice of, melting in the mouth, foie gras. Warm foie gras calls for a sweet Champagne whereas cold foie gras, opinioned Avner, is better with a Mombazillac. The perfect marriage between contrasting foods and their complimentary wines is fascinating 'food for conjecture'.

What Wine with What Food

I noticed a Californian Mondavi Red on the Wine List which was excellent value at £8.00 a bottle. It would go extremely well with the Entrée which was going to be Duck. A Champagne to complement Game would need to have a big, full flavour that would open up in the mouth. The Sir Winston Churchill vintage '82, a pale lemon gold with a refined mousse and a subtly perfumed bouquet with, if my oenological memory serves me correctly, hints of ginger and lemon, would make a perfect partner to ...

The Ballerina Duck

Duck is a traditionally fatty meat unless it is a Barbary breed which has a thin skin and acquires little fat during its lifetime. This Barbary likes movement, flying, cavorting and pirouetting in prevailing breezes coupled with energetic splash landings keep it slim and supple until it ends up attractively displayed on a large plate, fan sliced and pink served on a light sauce made from juices of blood oranges mingled with duck juices from the pan, accompanied with white asparagus tips and al dente mange tout. This was a Duck for Slender Gourmets.

Ronald Reagan's Favourite Dessert

Ronald Reagan's Inaugural Cuisine featured many star Chefs.

Avner's controversial dessert, Chocolate Ancho Chili Icecream was a big hit. I hope to see it on the Menu along with other dishes that might have appeared at The White House.

In the mean time, choose from one of the current star-spangled desserts, Brandy Snaps layered with raspberries and aniseed cream, or Mint cream layers in a tulip shell with a chocolate cream sauce.

'The Restaurant' might feature favourite dishes of personalities such as Ronald Reagan's Icecream and The Slender Gourmet's Ballerina Duck.

Price à la Carte around £18 to £25 for three courses.

Le Soufflé Restaurant at the Hotel Inter-Continental, Hyde Park Corner

The Inter-Continental is one of a coterie of five-star de luxe hotels, situated at Hyde Park Corner. Built in the seventies, this magnificent stone and glass 'palace' commands exciting panoramic views of Hyde Park, the Queen's Garden at Buckingham Palace, the Duke of Wellington's London home (Apsley House), and a statue of Boadicea triumphantly driving her chariot and charging horses that crowns Hyde Park Arch.

This hotel, conceived on the 'grande' scale, with its myriad lit foyer, creates a feeling of understated wealth and opulence, which gives way to elegant informality in Le Soufflé Bar where one can study the menu, at leisure, over a glass of Laurent Perrier.

Peter Kromberg, one of the world's leading Chefs who has won many culinary distinctions, is a Member of the Academie Culinaire de France and Honorary President of Les Toques Blanches. He has been the maître Chef de Cuisine since the hotel and Le Soufflé opened in 1975.

Cuisine de Vie

Peter joined us and spoke enthusiastically about the new 'Cuisine de Vie' which is appearing on the Menu alongside classical French dishes.

So much has been said by doctors and health advisers about heart and cholesterol and how everyone eats too much animal fat and salt, that it is reassuring to know that Chefs have our health, as well as our palates in mind, when they formulate new cuisines. Happily, the two elements, nutritious eating and gourmet predilections, when interpreted by a great Chef like Peter, go hand in hand.

For example, to 'commencer' – tender young vegetables tossed in vegetable broth, fresh cheese and truffle sauce, garnished with a crisp rissole of wild mushrooms. This combines healthy produce with exotic flavours.

Peter said that salt is such a strong condiment it kills rather then enhances natural flavours. His grandmother used natural salt substitutes, which today we are just rediscovering, like lemon juice and dried basil to bring out inherent food flavours.

Animal fats can be replaced with vegetable fats, and there is a choice of oils ranging from the very best French and Italian cold pressed, extra Virgin (the French is lighter than the Italian) to the lesser known grape and mustard seed and most exotic of all, truffle oil, wonderful for perfuming salads.

A Salmon Tasting

Unique to Le Soufflé is the 'Smoker' for smoking salmon. A mix of ash, oak and pine wood chips are used which gives the fish an individual aroma and taste. A comparison could be experienced with the Petite finesse de Saumon, a plate of three salmons – one, home-smoked with Beluga caviar (you can detect the mix of smoked chippings), another, Scandinavian gravadlax on a sweet mustard sauce, and the third, potted smoked salmon with fresh coriander and a tartare of salmon with Keta caviar.

When we entered the Restaurant, low lights and, in the evening, candles softened the linear design of the Art deco interior in a manner reminiscent of the days of luxury ocean-crossing liners. Tables and chairs are well spaced, comfortable and luxurious providing a perfect background to the art of eating, and at night, indulging in Peter's sybaritic, but portion-controlled, seven-course Choix du Chef.

Do Trifle with a Soufflé

Le Soufflé is famous for its soufflés and Peter has created a large variety varying from savoury to sweet.

Pour commencer: smoked haddock soufflé and mustard.

For a main course: sole and lobster soufflé with caviar and chive Champagne sauce.

As a vegetable accompanying an entrée, such as the sautéed fillet of veal, the leek and bacon soufflé served with a cream of mushroom sauce is an ideal accompaniment.

Next time, Peter is going to make a special Slender Gourmet Soufflé using an edible container instead of the customary china ramikin. A globular artichoke will be denuded of its interior and refilled with a soufflé mix including the artichoke bottom, foie gras and truffles. I can't wait!

Most people have soufflés at the end of the meal, the favourites being, a rum, raisin and banana soufflé with coffee sauce. You could try a chocolate and candied kumquats soufflé with light whipped cream. Or, less sweet, a plain soufflé flavoured with a choice of liqueur.

The sweet trolley as displayed by Maître d'Hotel, Josef Lanser, (a member of the Academie des Arts de la Table) is highly tempting, especially when Josef paints a decorative pattern on a white dessert plate with colours from six different fruit coulis. This provides the base for your choice of dessert which could be a delightfully rich and fluffy chocolate mousse; a tarte tatin or a selection of fruit compotes.

A popular luncheon venue with hotel visitors, business executives, small party groups and couples up from the Shires or home counties who enjoy the delights of the table followed by a cultural visit to the Royal Academy and conclude a perfect day with a visit to the theatre. As an alternative, instead of lunch, try the ...

Banquet for Slender Gourmets

For those evenings when we hanker after a splendid multi-course meal with one delicious taste sensation following another, reserve your favourite table at Le Soufflé, put your palate in Peter's hands and be surprised with the 7-course Choix du Chef. Do allow a few hours to bask in delicious food, Champagne, perfect service and your companion(s).

Each course is small, low in calories, high in nutrients, portion-controlled, so they will not play havoc with either your health or waistline.

Peter changes his menu every three or four days, depending on the availability of the finest and freshest produce in the world's markets.

The evening I went, we started with red Mullet steamed over seaweed with tomato petals and fennel, which looked very pretty. Another dish was the seafood chipolatas on a bed of puréed potatoes with veal sauce.

The dish I can only describe as 'heavenly' was the entrée. This was preceded by a mouth-watering sorbet made from blackcurrants, Crème de Cassis and a Mercury wine from Beaujolais. The 'heavenly' entrée was sautéed layers of Black Angus fillets of beef with fresh foie gras and a fresh truffle sauce, the perfume of which wafted up my nostrils completely captivating my olfactory glands.

A refreshing dessert which followed the Cheese Trolley was an Orange Flan with a blood orange coulis.

This is a 'Banquet' for those who want to eat the finest, freshest food, a cuisine that satisfies the soul and nourishes the body.

Le Menu du Jour (which changes daily) is £24.00
The Choix du Chef is £40.00
A la Carte between £25 and £35.00

Overtons, St James's

Standing at the bottom of St James's looking up towards Piccadilly, on your right you will notice four discreet Edwardian shop-fronts. One is the old established Wine firm of Berry Brothers; then, Lock & Co., hattier to the nobility; and, at the other end of the physical frame, Lobb, bootier and shoe-maker. In between these shops, all carrying the Royal Warrant, is the most interesting of all, 'Overtons', purveyors of superb cuisine and fine wines.

Inside you receive an immediate impression of colour, brightness and elegant design. Recently restyled, the original Oyster Bar has now been replaced with four large comfortable booths much favoured by business executives for lunches and romantic trysts in the evenings.

The main restaurant has a cheerful atmosphere greatly enhanced by an army of waiters who pass to and fro, bearing offerings of plump oysters, smoked salmon, laden platters of prawns, crab, smoked eel, lobster, sole, turbot, fish cakes and fish pie, but above all, Overtons are famous for their Oysters.

The Reluctant Mollusk

Oysters don't like to come out of their shells. Prising the mollusk apart at home can lead to hand injuries and frayed tempers, resorting to a hammer, chisel or pneumatic drill will only give the oyster a headache and yourself a great deal of aggro. That is why they are best eaten in restaurants where they can be opened by experts.

The Sex Life of the Oyster

Oysters have the reputation of constantly changing their sex – they are also regarded as an aphrodisiac – the world's great lovers' concern with sex, and their libidos going down when they should be going up, have been persuaded that the remedy lies in the high sperm count derived from the oyster's high zinc content. Casanova 'in the interests of science', was reputed to have eaten 150 at one sitting, and then did a count with the aid of a magnifying glass and decided to keep oysters on his diet.

How to Eat an Oyster

There are two schools of thought. One, place it on the tongue and press the oyster against the palate long enough for the flavour to come through, then swallow. The other school recommends chewing to release the flavour and to avoid indigestion which would be badly impaired if you swallowed a bivalve containing a pearl. Head Oysterman Michael at Scotts showed me his collection of both black and white pearls which he has accumulated over the years.

Oysters taste of the waters in which they fatten, the purer the water the more desirable the oyster. A lot of Overton's oysters come from England's finest Oyster beds in Poole and Colchester, also from County Cork in Ireland. Flavours vary, so why not choose a mixed half dozen ranging from Imperials to Natives.

To test whether the oyster is alive, squeeze a touch of lemon on its beard, if it palpitates, it is alive and is the freshest food you can eat.

Haute Cuisine Oysters

I am one of the extreme minority that prefers oysters cooked. Louis of Overtons, immediately suggested that I have half a dozen prepared in the classic Escoffier manner, either Florentine with spinach, or Mornay with a parmesan cheese sauce. I find the cooked oyster far more succulent than the raw bivalve.

Medical opinion now says that a moderate consumption of cream, butter and cheese is not harmful. As these are the basic ingredients for haute cuisine sauces and every Diet has to have its little splurge, I chose Oysters Mornay which were delicious as prepared by Overton's talented Chef, Domingo Chinarro.

Composing the Menu

Oysters Mornay should be followed with an entrée without another sauce, perhaps a plate of wild smoked salmon. The wild salmon unlike the farmed, is full of flavour as the fish is caught when swimming upstream, a hard exercise which makes it lean and low in fats. When smoked correctly, in brick holes over seasoned oak chippings, the flavour is superb.

I had Lobster which would have been low in fat and calories if I had chosen it grilled or poached in a court-bouillon, but I didn't, I had Lobster Themidor.

Lobster, Alive, 'Alive O'

Before the Lobster is cooked, I appreciate a 'live showing' at the table. Louis understood, and within two minutes a procession of waiters returned with two beautiful two-pounders reclining on a silver platter. One of them gave a spirited performance, waving his claws and attacking a slice of bread with a deft pincer movement including the waiter's finger. The next time I saw him, his dark deep seaweed green shell had turned a pretty shade of pink, his meat was dressed with a Béchamel sauce to which had been added mustard and, as a final farewell, flambéed with brandy. He was utterly delicious.

The House Champagne which is Lanson cut the richness of the sauces, as did the bowl of mixed berries which concluded my meal.

Who is the Mystery Artist?

Admiring the painting on Overton's Menu Cover depicting a group of happy gastronomes enjoying the last stages of a sumptuous repast, yet still looking longingly at beautiful plates of food and wine; I wondered who was the artist? If you can guess the name of the famous cartoonist you might win a bottle of Champagne.

A la Carte – between £15 to £35 depending on choice.

'Celebrities' at The Hampshire Hotel, Leicester Square

Leicester Square, the scene of theatre and cinema land, has long needed a five-star hotel. Celebrities Bar and Restaurant in The Hampshire attracts visitors, business executives and showbiz personalities. Famous Impressarios, Directors, Prima Ballerinas from Covent Garden, visiting Divas from The Coliseum, just over the road, actors, actresses, pop stars and the glitterati that attend movie premières all drop into 'Celebrities' to be revived with perhaps a Golden Gielgud Cocktail, a Curtain Call or a First Night.

In the Gay Nineties, Leicester Square was famous for its Music Halls and 'larger than life' characters like George Leybourne of 'Champagne Charlie' fame. Easily recognizable by his shining black topper, white striped trousers and coat trimmed with fur, he would dash in a carriage drawn by four white horses from Music Hall to Restaurant, to dine stylishly in surroundings very much like 'Celebrities' have created today.

'Celebrities' captures the gaiety and opulence of the Edwardian heyday in its richly furnished restaurant with dark panelled walls generously covered with paintings of the period. Wall-to-wall lush red-and-gold patterned carpets are offset with luxuriantly scalloped curtains. Comfortable settees and chairs in gold and green, invite you to sit at tables draped with red damask cloths covered with whiter-than-white linen on which sparkle silver place settings and large twinkling glasses. A plenitude of classical Chinese vases provide 'Overtures of the Orient'.

The IN Champagne at the turn of the century was Perrier-Jouët's Belle Epoque which comes in the beautiful flower-decorated bottle. So what better choice than a bottle of this nectar to put you into the mood of the Naughty Nineties.

Both the Menu of the Day and the à la Carte offer intriguing taste experiences. A cold hors d'oeuvre might be 'a Slipper of Bacon and Parsley Terrine with Red Cabbage'. A hot hors d'oeuvre could be 'a Mousseline of Crab with Asparagus and Chervil Butter Sauce'.

Soup – Beautiful Soup

Colin Button, the Chef, excels in creating unusual Soups, a Jerusalem Artichoke with little Welsh Rarebits; or a Cream of Red Pimento with Almond Pancakes.

I chose the Pigeon Consommé with Goose Liver Gnocchi. Colin, who is a specialist in game, favours the French pigeons from Anjou which are bred for their delicate (rather than strong gamey) flavour. The gnocci is made from choux pastry mixed with a little foie gras and poached in the Consommé. It is slenderizing, approximately 70 cals, full of purity and protein it was a satisfying dish on its own, but being a great lover of food I couldn't stop at just one course.

The Vegetarian section which applies to both Menus, is most imaginative, I shall have to return to try the Roast Celeriac Tart with Wood Mushroom and Truffle Sauce.

Celebrities

Perrier-Jouët-Belle Epoque

Dishes with unexpected embellishment like seaweed noodles (full of iron), brioche herb toppings (much more interesting than breadcrumbs), and glazed minted baby turnips (a welcome change from the often tasteless boiled potato) delight with their novelty.

The entrées feature unusual cuts like Slippers, Shanks and Skirts. This stems from Colin's early apprenticeship to a Master Butcher where he soon became an expert on all aspects of meat. Later, at Buckingham Palace, The Royal Garden Hotel and at the legendary Gleneagles, he put this knowledge to good use by recreating old English dishes, which used these cuts, like the Skirt of Beef marinated in oil, red wine and herbs, grilled and served with an Anchovy Sauce. (This may have been a Royal favourite.) The marriage of meat with fish is very traditional, like adding oysters to a steak and kidney pie.

Game is Popular

During the Season the Menu abounds with Game – Grouse, Pheasant, Partridge, Quails, Pigeons, Squabs, Rabbit, Hare, Wild Boar and Venison. Colin gets the Fallow Deer, a breed developed for its flavour and tenderness, it spends two happy years in pastures and woods and then is speedily sent to the Big Deer Park in the Sky with one swift, accurately fired shot. It lives and dies happy, and ends up either as a medallion, or slipper, often served with a sauce made from crushed juniper berries and Pineau de Charente liqueur, which perfumes and intensifies the flavour of the meat.

A Super Sausage

For a main course I chose Colin's superlative Saucisson de Homard et de Crevettes with a Sauce Kari, a dish he must have created with Slender Gourmets in mind as it is fat free. Most sausages are unhealthy as they contain preservatives, flavour enhancers, animal fat and, worst of all, the filling is forced into skins made from plastic. The body cannot rid itself of artificial materials and eating a manmade fibre like plastic causes a build-up of toxics in joints and tissues which could lead to rheumatism and cellulite.

Fish Sausages are an inspired change from the customary pork or beef. Whole lobster meat and prawns is flavoured with basil and a hint of garlic. No preservatives are needed as they are prepared daily, and most important, the skins are made from natural animal membranes.

Two large sausages with a Coconut Curry Sauce and the most exquisitely cooked Wild Canadian Rice sautéed with shallots and then cooked in a fish stock sent me into a gastronomical seventh heaven.

The Cheese Trolley offers a varied range which come from Auguste Marechal, a family firm with a big reputation in Lyon, who buy directly from farms in the Auvergne, Jura and Comte. These unpasteurized Cheeses have so much more pungency and character than the customary pasteurized variety. The most delicious of all, a triple cream, comes from the Champagne area and is the Chaource – eat it lingeringly with a handful of black grapes.

Eat it on; Exercise it off

If you succumb to the desserts, the Three Shaded Chocolate (white, dark and bitter) mousse filled with frais du bois (little wild strawberries with a taste of woodlands) is sumptuous, but be wise and plan on doing an extra three rounds of the Champagne Charlie Quartet on page 89 the next morning. If you eat it on; you have to exercise it off.

Spin me a Coronet

Colin has promised me a special dessert made from white spun sugar, fattening, unhealthy and full of empty calories, so why am I eating it? The answer is, I am not – I plan to wear it instead!

He is going to spin me a Coronet which I shall put on my head when I take a curtain call in the company of a Champagne Compatriot at The Coliseum later this year.

At 'Celebrities' the Curtain rises seven days a week.

Dishes from the à la Carte often appear on the Daily Menu which is £17.50 for lunch and £24.00 for Dinner.

Le Chateau Restaurant at The May Fair Hotel, Berkeley Street
Romance in Mayfair

Ever since a Nightingale sang in Berkeley Square within serenading distance of The May Fair Hotel, that particular part of London has long been associated with dreams of love.

The first pull at the heart strings is looking into the florist on the corner of Berkeley Square that always has window-after-window full of the largest, most gorgeous flowers imaginable.

Then there is the glamorous Motor-car Showroom opposite The May Fair Hotel full of Rolls, Daimlers, Jaguars all shimmering and sleek, just waiting for a beautiful person to sit behind the wheel and whizz down Piccadilly.

The final touch of wistful nostalgia occurs crossing the lobby into the Cocktail Bar where Iain will be playing a selection of songs from 'Love Affair'.

Over a glass of 'poo' (Laurent Perrier is the House Champagne) you begin to revive and think about 'falling in love again ...' All this can happen at any time of the year, but especially during the month of February when thoughts and menus turn to St Valentine's Day.

Spring is in the air and the world of commerce is momentarily forsaken for 'dreams of love'. Men rush out to buy red roses, perfume, heart-shaped boxes of chocolates for their wives, sweethearts, girl friends and loved ones. Restaurants aware of the occasion plan a celebratory evening with special dishes created by their Chefs.

Le Chateau is one of the most charming restaurants in London: modelled on the spacious dining-room of a luxurious French Chateau, it is a room that weaves and curves, creating secluded corners and arbours, as well as opening out on to a lively restaurant scene.

On St Valentine's evening the room was filled with pretty round tables for two, floor-length white linen cloths with sparkling silver and glass place settings, a bowl of pink flowers and a candle on every table, and for each lady a long-stemmed red rose.

It Has to be Pink

There can only be one choice on St Valentine's Day – it has to be Pink Champagne, the most romantic drink in the world – under its influence women become radiantly beautiful and men incredibly handsome and dashing. Charles de Cazanove's (not to be confused with Cazanova) Brut Rosé with its sparkling salmon pink colour would be an excellent choice.

As you raise your glass and watch the bubbles spiral to the surface, you can also gaze into your companion's eyes. Eyes can be more eloquent than words. While delicately nosing the bouquet and reestablishing eye contact, you need to decide whether you are getting blackcurrants, yeast, grapes, a flirtatious twinkle or maybe a deep yearning regard. Sip, taste, swallow, experience the pleasure of the moment and then, savour the long, lingering after-taste.

The special six-course Valentine's Menu started with 'Lovers Delight' a medley of mussels and lobster with asparagus tips.

'Blossoming Romance' followed, a delicious grilled Turbot Supreme criss-crossed golden with butter, served with sprouting lentils and herbs.

We then had a 'Passionate Pause' passion fruit sorbet, when our fingers briefly intertwined.

Iain was playing 'Love Affair in Mayfair', one of his own compositions inspired by a real romance that happened in Le Chateau. An American visitor fell in love with the lady clarinettist who led the musical ensemble at the Sunday Brunch. A year later he returned on St Valentine's Day, proposed, and their wedding celebrations took place in The Crystal Room in 1987, the year of The May Fair's Golden Jubilee (plus ten years).

Love makes the world go round, but one also needs a great Chef and a highly efficient kitchen to provide the food for love.

Below Stairs

In the kitchens a different scenario develops. Orders are phoned down to a battery of Chefs who work quickly and dexterously, cooking, arranging and plating the dishes. The Chef de Cuisine, Michael Coaker, stands on one side of a ten foot long Serving Galley. On the other side five Chefs are poised for action. Behind them is a ten foot long kitchen range of gas jets, ovens, hot plates and an eye-level electric grill – no microwave or sous vide in sight, thank goodness.

The hot line from the restaurant rings down and Michael, like the conductor of an orchestra, transmits the order to the waiting band of Chefs.

The symphony starts: Chefs spring into action, oven doors fly open, there is some quick stirring from the saucier, sizzling sounds from pans on gas jets, herbs are sprinkled, and the five Chefs dart professionally hither and thither with some deft foot work to avoid bumping into each other. The dish is garnished and plated, waiting for the Maestro's approval. Then the tureen is on in a flash, the commis skids to a standstill, and is ready to rush it to the restaurant where it will be courteously served by a waiter who, at the appropriate moment, will whisk off the tureen cover to reveal our fourth course – St Valentine's Proposal – in this case Breast of Duck with mango and woodland mushrooms. My choice was Rosettes of Lamb with an aubergine mousse.

A 'Tender Kiss' (farmhouse cheeses) followed the Proposal, and to crown it all we had a 'Sweethearts Accolade', an Ice Souffle of citrus fruits in a chocolate case.

This was followed by coffee, petits fours and light-hearted conversation.

You don't have to wait until St Valentine's Day every time you want a romantic interlude, because there is a regular 'Menu Gourmet' of six small delicious courses, at £32.50 per head.

A Sunday Highlight

I recommend the Sunday Brunch which at £19.50 per head is excellent and includes a Bloody Mary or Bucks Fizz.

Four courses starting with a help-yourself from a most attractive salad bar displaying charcuterie, smoked meats and fish including, when I was there, my favourite giant Dublin Bay Prawns.

For the next course I was torn between Eggs Benedict or Eggs New Orleans (garnished with crab).

Traditional Roast ribs of Beef from the Trolley – or if you feel a bit oriental – Tempura Scampi with stir fried vegetables, are just two from a choice of eight entrées.

Desserts from the Trolley, and the Cheese Trolley (the unpasteurized choice is superb) complete your repast.

All this and music from the four-piece ensemble and Sunday lunchtime becomes the highlight of the day.

The Halcyon Restaurant at the Halcyon Hotel, Holland Park, W.11

To find a country house hotel, within jogging distance (200 yards) of Holland Park and roughly two miles (as the Crow flies) from Marble Arch, is a rarity.

'The Halcyon Hotel' is named after the mythical bird of antiquity which built its nest on calm, unruffled waters where peace and tranquillity prevail.

The name suits this elegant stuccoed building which has been beautifully restored to blend in unassumingly with the many imposing private Millionaire and Ambassadorial residences in the area.

Halcyon Days

'The Halycon Restaurant' extends through large French windows on to an ornamental garden and patio.

White wrought-iron furniture, elegantly clothed tables laid with vases of flowers, sparkling china and glasses greet the eye. Wisteria and roses planted between the flagstones clamber up the walled trellises to the first floor balconied suites and rooms.

Four large and three small tables, all shaded from the English sun with picturesque umbrellas, provide spacious eating facilities for twenty-two people.

Ambience is Important

Everyone occasionally needs to unwind and get away from the stressful pace of modern life; eating outdoors in beautiful surroundings is one of the answers.

My first suggestion is a glass of Champagne (the Halcyon's House favourite is Taittinger), watching and listening to the bubbles as they twinkle and effervesce under the caressing rays of the sun, immediately has a relaxing effect.

My second suggestion, if you are an aspiring Slender Gourmet and counting the calories, is to choose from the list of Starters rather than follow the conventional pattern of starter, main, cheese and dessert.

Not on the Menu but a seasonal inspiration of the Chef's was a cold Soup made from puréed Ogen Melon and sun-dried Tomatoes which are full of natural concentrated sweetness.

Tataki of Beef, strips of fillet steak, cooked by marination in a soya sauce and chili peppers and served on a bed of shaved white radish is a balanced combination of protein and root vegetable, the crispness and bite of the vegetable offsetting the succulent tenderness of the peppered Beef. A Slimmer's Winner on all counts.

This could be followed by another starter, a choice of sixteen allows for balanced Menu computations.

Tagliatelle (a little pasta is good for the health) prepared in the Southern Mediterranean style with generous quantities of black olives crushed to a thick paste, sun-dried Tomatoes and basil. Again, a delicious Slimmer's Winner.

To conclude, Passion Fruit Brulée, a smooth crême covered by crunchy burnt toffee topping. Alternatively, refreshing to the palate, light on the waistline, would be a sorbet made from fresh fruits of the Season.

Halcyon Nights

Once described by the *Los Angeles Times* as 'London's best kept secret' the Halcyon has become the favourite place to stay with celebrities from the world of film and music, notably Marlon Brando, Richard Harris, Lauren Bacall, Michael Douglas, Tina Turner and Kevin Costner, to name but a few.

The Bedrooms and Suites are all individually decorated and furnished to a very high standard. I particularly loved the Halcyon Suite with its shimmering silk-tented ceiling and its extra large four-poster bed. I was tempted to follow the advice of a great courtesan who attributed her lasting beauty to the fact that she never stood when she could sit, and would never sit if she could lie down.

Music, Magnums and Canapés

The Conservatory, also part of the Suite, is particularly stunning with its lovely view of trees, garden and flowery arbours. A popular venue for Cocktail parties accommodating up to eighty people.

On such an occasion the best troubadour would be the Nightingale if he could be persuaded to sing at the requisite hour.

Magnums are practical for parties over ten people being not only an economic way to buy Champagne, but because the wine matures better in large bottles. The visual effect has 'instant impact'.

The hotel makes a feature of room service and will happily serve cocktail Canapés, even extending to more robust dishes like Eggs Benedict which are excellent.

The Halcyon is open all year round; the Terrace from beginning of April until Winter sets in.

Starters average between £3 to £6
Main Courses between £8 and £12
Desserts £3.50

British Airways – Concorde – The Cuisine of the Skies

Since Concorde flies twice as fast as the Speed of Sound would dinner be over before it had started? After all, the 7.00 p.m. London departure arrives New York time at 6.00 the same evening – an hour ahead of itself! What happens when Concorde breaks through the Sound Barrier? How would it feel flying at the incredible speed of 1,340 miles per hour at a height of 51,500 feet? How would the bubbles react in my glass, let alone how would I react to Supersonic dining?

The Concorde Club

These questions were going through my mind as I entered 'Speed Wing Lounge' at Heathrow Airport, known to its regular travellers as 'The Club'. First time 'Concordians', like myself, were discreetly eyeing one another, wondering if the other person was maybe a famous celebrity, pop star, film star, statesman or a high flying business executive who sped around the world attending dynamic meetings.

Concorde carries 100 passengers who were gradually arriving and refreshing themselves from a generous array of drinks provided at the Bar which included two Champagnes, a Lanson non-vintage and a Pommery '81 named after the Champagne House's founder, Louise Pommery. This Connoisseur's Choice is chic, and expensive looking, with a 22-carat gold shimmer, which sparkles along the tongue before bidding a lingering 'adieu'.

The Graceful Albatross

Concorde is both elegant in appearance, and a tribute, to sophisticated engineering and supreme technology. It has been likened to a pre-historic phantom Pterosaur with a hooked reptilian beak. Sitting on the tarmac, it looked like some gigantic silvery bird. Boarding Concorde, seating arrangements are in pairs on either side of the gangway, was the start to a great adventure.

We were off! Soaring along the runway at something like 250 miles an hour, a breathtaking experience, accelerating all the time until we became airborne and skimmed through the clouds into the blue sky above.

The Concorde Cellar

The actual flying time is three hours and twenty minutes which can be spent looking out the window daydreaming into the blue of a limitless sky, or tasting a variety of fine wines specially selected for Concorde by an expert Committee, including Michael Broadbent and Hugh Johnson, whose knowledge of Wine is legendary.

Full-bodied Grand Cru Classe Clarets, like Château Talbot and Château Lynch-Bages, white Puligny-Montrachets from fabled Communes and Vineyards such as Close de la Mouchère and Les Folatières, vie with powerful red Burgundy's from Nuits-Saint-George and Beaune.

Champagne is Good for You

My favourite, served throughout the flight, was Pol Roger, Cuvée Sir Winston Churchill brut vintage '82. The bubbles and myself, flying at a height of 51,500 feet, might have been affected, but we both maintained our effervescence, which, according to research conducted by two French doctors, is due to health-giving 'oligo-elements' and important minerals like zinc, lithium, potassium and magnesium found in Champagne – so drink, and enjoy that extra glass, was my advice to myself.

The Cuisine of the Skies

It is not every day that one can Dine literally on 'Top of the World' and be able to see the curve of the earth's surface whilst nibbling Lobster, Smoked Sturgeon, or Veal and Ham Canapés. Each Canapé a taste sensation in itself, including a pastry boat generously filled with Caviar. As Kurt Hafner, Chief of Catering Standards, explained, British Airways is always striving for perfection, for the freshest, and best possible produce, and the 'slightly unusual' with which to tempt the Concorde 'high flyers'. One of these was an intriguing appetizer, fillets of lightly Smoked Salmon, cut in wedges, like orange segments, served with golden Oscietra Caviar which turned out to be a highly original dish.

Everything down to the smallest detail; fine damask table linen and Royal Doulton China, decorated with Concorde's individual Royal Blue and Silver Band, is in perfect harmony.

Guest Chef, Anton Mosimann of 'Mosimann's Belgravia Dining Club'

Alongside their own team of top award-winning Chefs, British Airways occasionally engage great culinary talents to create dishes which will further enhance their Menu.

Dinner consisted of six courses, three of which were marked with the Mosimann logo. King Prawns served Japanese style, with an oriental sauce garnished with two types of contrasting coloured seaweed and poppy seeds was one of them.

The second course was Breast of Chicken with Mushrooms in filo pastry, Spinach subric (Spinach puréed with reduced Béchamel shaped into moulds) and Asparagus Spears parcelled into bundles wrapped with lean Ham. Whilst savouring this delicacy I noticed green lights flashing on the passenger indicator screen. Leaning forward to see what was happening I discovered that we were about to break through The Sound Barrier at 700 plus miles an hour. I waited for what I thought would be the 'Big Bang' or at least a 'small whimper', but we continued smoothly with neither jolt nor tremble. Travelling faster than the Speed of Sound, the 'Big Bang' was happening in space way behind us.

Combining well with Concorde's cruising speed of 1,340 miles an hour was the dessert, a terrine of seasonal fruit with Mango and Orange sauce.

Guest Chef, Franz Klampfer of The Pierre Hotel in New York

If you ever yearned to dine at one of Manhattan's top restaurants, the legendary 'Pierre', then Concorde, on its return New York to London flight, provides the opportunity to sample dishes prepared by their Chef, Franz Klampfer in conjunction with a Menu created by British Airways own culinary star, Wolfgang Stoll.

Hotel Pierre feature an 'alternative cuisine' which allows Gourmets full indulgence as their dishes are nutritionally balanced, low in calories, cholesterol, sodium and fats.

A perfect example was Mignon of Beef served on Eggplant ovals surrounded by Artichoke confit with Pearl Onions and sun-dried Tomatoes. This married well with Château Latour's second selection, Les Forts de Latour 1975, described as 'possessing flavours both lean and deep, resinous and silky, refreshing and concentrated which linger luxuriously'. Feeling sublimely relaxed one can then quietly contemplate the wonders of the Universe, the Moon rising on one side of Concorde whilst the Sun sets on the other.

The Concorde Experience Continues ...

After landing at JFK Airport, a British Airways courtesy helicopter takes you to the centre of Manhattan. There you might care to book into a de luxe Slender Gourmet recommended hotel such as 'The Pierre' facing Central Park on fashionable 5th Avenue, or 'The Ritz Carlton' on Central Park South. Both relatively small hotels but traditional in the classic European style, offering unsurpassed views of Central Park, spear-pointed by slender soaring skyscrapers. One of the most dynamic, dramatic skylines in the world. Alternatively, 'The Plaza Athénée' situated a block away from Central Park on East 64th Street is another elegant hotel popular with the British Royal Family. Prince Charles, Princess Diana and the Duke and Duchess of York are frequent visitors.

The *QE2* – Princess Grill II – Dining on the High Seas

The *QE2* is one of the world's largest luxury liners. Her size is staggering; her beauty inspiring. She appears to grow out of the water like a mountain, thirteen decks high, soaring upwards, topped by an imperious black-and-red funnel.

Once on board you get lost in a maze of public rooms, sumptuous lounges, elegant cocktail bars, five restaurants including a midnight buffet by the outdoor swimming-pool, a casino, a library, the famous Golden Door Health Spa and a theatre seating 500 people.

She carries 1,800 passengers – and almost as many crew – who reside in cabins, staterooms, and even penthouse suites.

Whether it be a Mediterranean, Scandinavian or world cruise or crossing the Atlantic, the *QE2* offers the ultimate in a Champagne Lifestyle; elegant travel, coupled with extravagant dining.

Extravagant dining can deplete your pocket, but not when you travel on the high seas. The world is your oyster and whether it be Caviar, Smoked Salmon, the choicest cuts of prime Kansas Beef, or exotic delicacies like Baby Suckling Pig or Bird's Nest Soup, your wish is Cunard's command. You can indulge, gourmet-style, in either The Princess or Queen's Grill.

The newly opened Princess Grill II is a beautifully appointed room seating approximately 100 guests. Nine large picture windows offer fantastic views of the sea which can vary dramatically in mood, from exciting ocean swells to tranquillity-inducing calm waters in sheltered harbours. If you suffer from 'queasiness', remember that the ship's stabilizers keep guests, waiters, food, plates and glasses on an even keel, which makes dining a pleasure in all weather.

The ship's daily newspaper suggests appropriate dress for the evening, formal for the Captain's Gala Dinner, and casual or 'optional' wear on less auspicious occasions. Daily dinner menus are often based around the cuisine of a particular country, which could be Italian, British, American or international.

The French dinner was perfect for Slender Gourmets offering amongst its six courses, *Les Oeufs au Caviar* – Shirred Eggs topped with Vodka Cream and Malassol Caviar, *Escargot* (snails) *en Brioche, Filet de Boeuf flambée au Poivre vert* and *Chausson aux Pommes flambée* – Apple Strudel flamed with Kirsch and Calvados.

The Virgin Sturgeon needs no urgin' …

So goes the ditty and since she gives birth to thousands of eggs in one go she could be described as being sensuously licentious. Cunard purchases approximately twenty per cent of the world's supply of Beluga Caviar, of which a generous consignment finds its way to the Princess Grill.

Caviar is an ideal substance for slimmers, 1 oz (75 cals) should be taken twice daily with Champagne. This could be followed, at lunchtime, with Steak Tartar, well-hung fillet of Kansas Beef, to which Johnathon Smith (Assistant Maître d'hôtel) recommends adding 'oomph' ingredients such as spices, shallots, capers, tabasco and brandy for added glamour. A variety of colourful leaves from the lettuce family, well-tossed with a vinaigrette dressing, will provide the necessary crisp texture to the dish. As a finale, an Ice Coupe with fresh raspberries.

Burn up your luncheon calories by exercising

A brisk promenade around the boat deck, 5 laps = 1 mile, followed by a swim in the pool and immersion in the hot, foamy 'steppes' of the Whirlpool. Arrange yourself so that the 'embonpoint' makes contact with the bubble jets which gently massage and tone up sleepy abdominals, whilst other bubble jets work away at fatty deposits and cellulite loitering on susceptible areas like thighs, hips and upper underarms.

Alternate hot and cold dunks do wonders for burning up calories, and make you feel like a millionaire, all set for the serious meal of the day – Dinner.

a memorable flambée evening

A Memorable Flambé Evening ...

Few restaurants cook at your table, douse the food with alcohol and set it alight. This is partly for fear of scorching the walls or setting off the fire alarm, which activates the ceiling sprinklers, which in turn would drench the diners. These minor hazards do not deter Cunard from practising the old gastronomic art of 'Flambé'.

One of the great 'flambéists' of all time was Oscar Bassam, a Fellow of the Acadamie Internationale de Flambier who won world-wide awards during his career on the *Queen Elizabeth* and her sister ship the *Queen Mary*, where he flambéed for many famous people including the Duke and Duchess of Windsor. He has since retired, but the tradition is carried on by Robert Beadle, the Maître d'Hôtel, and his assistant, Johnathon Smith, in the Princess Grill II. Entrées such as Steak Diane, Lobster Thermidor, Crayfish Cardinal and Chicken Chartreuse might be followed by mouthwatering desserts like Crêpe Suzette and Cherries Jubilee.

This drawing by Michael ffolkes captures Oscar, practically flambéeing The Slender Gourmet, at a Taittinger event launching their Comtes de Champagne, '79 vintage.

A trip on the *QE2* provides the ultimate in luxurious living as well as providing facilities for a healthy, outdoor life style. Fresh air and exercise coupled with extravagant eating for weight loss and pleasure is every Slender Gourmet's Dream.

Read on to discover the Slender Gourment restaurant recommendations.

The Jockey Club at The Ritz-Carlton, New York

One of the many advantages of staying at The Ritz-Carlton facing Central Park is that you can join the many joggers, walkers, deep breathers (the oxygen level in the air is good) and fitness enthusiasts who take to the Park for their early morning workout. On your return you can 'boost' yourself for the day with a Joggers or Japanese breakfast which makes a change from the customary Continental or American.

This exquisitely furnished hotel with 280 rooms offers luxurious accommodation, personal service and hospitality in the tradition of that great hotelier Cesar Ritz.

The Jockey Club

A popular meeting spot for New Yorkers and celebrities in the evenings is The Jockey Club Bar, tended by a Damon Runyon-type character called Norman

Bukofzer who resembles a cross between Gene Wilder and Harpo Marx. He shakes a cocktail to a Rumba beat with Marakas-like arm movements. His Brooklynese quips come fast and racy, you would have to be very dour not to be warmed and amused by his humour.

Putting on The Ritz

The Jockey Club Restaurant is so beautiful that you really feel like dressing your 'elegant best' in order to complement the eighteenth- and nineteenth-century Grand Country House surroundings, which include an extensive Art Collection.

Chef Tom Parlo creates his own Continental and American dishes often adding Italian and Asian embellishments. His mouth-watering creations include the famous Jockey Club Crab Cakes with corn and bellpepper sauce, and wild rice fritters.

Studying the Menu I noticed that some of the dishes were marked with small heart signs. This indicates that they have been prepared in accordance with the recommendations of the American Heart Association to reduce dietary fat, cholesterol and to control calories.

For 342 calories you can dine on Fresh Pine Island Oysters in a chive and shallot vinegar sauce, a mere 54 calories. Grilled free-range Chicken breast with tomato coulis and tarragon 182 calories. A dessert of poached pear with an apple and raspberry coulis 99 calories.

Keeping within 500 calories you could vary the entrée and have Heart of Beef with Truffles and a Pinot Noir Sauce which was utterly delicious and totted up 34.9 grams of protein; 4.1% fat; 232 calories. However, I strayed and started with Cream of Cauliflower Soup garnished with Poached Oysters and lingered over Banana Fritters graced with fresh banana Icecream.

I tried a sparkling wine made under the auspices of one of the great names in Champagne, Domaine Mumm from California's Napa Valley. It was very good, but there is no substitute for Champagne, and no substitute for premier quality which is where the Ritz-Carlton excels.

The Four Seasons Restaurant at 99 East 52nd Street, New York

In the heart of Manhattan at Park Avenue and 52nd Street is 'The Four Seasons', rated as the City's most popular restaurant in the '89, '90 and '91 Zagat New York City Restaurant Survey coming 'tops' in all three categories:

Superb Food: Sophisticated American, Continental with Asian influences plus the food trend of the nineties, Gourmet Spa Cuisine.

Dramatic Decor: Architectural splendour, abstract design, sky high ceilings, rippling metal chain window draperies, a twenty-foot square marble pool, and an enormous sculptured stalactite in bronze suspended over The Bar.

Service: Ultra-professional and genuinely caring.

The Grill Room

With its soaring ceiling, leather banquettes and rosewood walls dramatized by a huge Picasso canvas, this is the 'In-Place' for The Power Lunch where the City's most prominent 'movers and shakers' gather. The 'In-Drink' – Aqua Minerale. The 'Out-Food' – Desserts.

The Pool Room

For Dining, The Pool Room is romantically inviting with its spaciously appointed tables, illuminated trees and colourful seasonal plants that surround the gurgling waters in the marble pool.

In this futuristic setting which epitomises the vitality and constant movement of contemporary New York, Alex von Bidder guided us through the Menu making some excellent suggestions.

I love Pasta but tend to steer away from carbohydrates. However, I was persuaded to try the house Ravioli. It was a revelation, light, wafer-thin pasta packages, full of succulent lobster and scallops proved to be a Slender Gourmet recommendation.

My companion chose Smoked Scotch Salmon Roulade with Caviar artistically arranged with sprigs of willowy Dill, which, she said, tasted even better than it looked.

It was the Season for a gourmet speciality which Alex felt we just had to 'squeeze in' between courses, soft-shelled Crab. The month of April is the Season when Crabs are young and their shells have not matured. The combination of a light 'al dente' crunch with the soft, white meat was delicious.

Chef Christian Albin likes to combine contrasting elements, like meat with fish. Veal Four Seasons is cooked with Crabmeat and Artichoke Hearts, which appealed to my friend. I, meantime, ran my eye down a most impressive Wine List.

The Four Seasons Wine Cellar have, since they opened thirty-two years ago, bought well and judiciously of old and rare wines which they are now in a position to pass on at a relatively low mark-up. The Buy of the Century must be the Pomerol that causes Connoisseur's knees to quiver, Chateau Petrus with its characteristic mulberry richness is on the Wine List, at well below World market prices, the '82 is only $275 a bottle and the more matured '76 $450, whereas a top London restaurant is charging over £1,000 a bottle for comparable vintages.

Alternatively, an excellent selection of American wines chosen by Paul Kovi include a Mondavi Pinot Noir '88 which married harmoniously with my entrée, Crisp Farmhouse Duck. It arrived at the table beautifully golden and crisp. Watching Alex carve with swift, dexterous movements was an art lesson in anatomy. Undecided whether to have the Poivre or Papaya sauce I had both, but preferred the refreshing tang of the fruit. Wild rice mixed with pine nuts was the perfect accompaniment.

The Food of the Nineties

It was interesting to talk with Paul Kovi, the owner, about his special Gourmet Spa Cuisine which he sees as the food trend of the nineties. Poached Sea Bass with Yucca and Hearts of Palm is a mouthwatering example.

This health-conscious Hungarian keeps his weight at attractive levels and would like to help his clientele do likewise. After consulting doctors and nutritionists, his Chefs now produce gourmet dishes balanced in vitamins, minerals, proteins and carbohydrates, using the minimum of saturated fats, artificial sweeteners and salt.

Good slimming advice comes from Oscar Wilde ... 'I have the simplest of tastes. I am always satisfied with the best.' This is what you will always find at The Four Seasons.

Windows on the World at The World Trade Center, New York

It is hard to visualize dining a quarter of a mile up in the sky on the 107th floor of the highest skyscraper in the world. A high speed elevator that takes sixty earpopping seconds, whizzed us into a trio of Restaurants known as 'Windows on the World'.

Walls of Wine

'The Cellar in the Sky' is a small jewel-box-like room, its walls, appropriately enough, consist of highrise racks of fine wines. The moon and stars and lights from thousands of twinkling skyscrapers are reflected through the bottles, creating warm and unusual patterns of light in which to examine the colour of the liquid in your glass.

Twice a month, thirty-six guests swirl, inhale, savour, sip, swallow, bite, nibble and taste their way through New York's most satisfying dining ritual. A superb seven-course dinner designed around five wines created by a trio of gastronomic stars, Chef Karl Schmid, Wine Director Kevin Zraly and Cellar Master Alec Brough will astound your taste buds, creating a memorable union of food and wine. To aid the 'degustation', a guitarist plays romantic classical music throughout the four-hour evening entertainment.

A most Spectacular Restaurant ...

The showpiece is 'The Restaurant', which is built in tiers that gradually descend as one gets closer to the windows, so that every table commands panoramic views of Manhattan and fifty-five miles beyond. Our table by the floor-to-ceiling windows offered fabulous views of illuminated landmarks like The Statue of Liberty, Staten Island, the Empire State Building and the Brooklyn Bridge, not to mention helicopters circling on par with the fiftieth floor and moving lights from toy-size cars transversing the Avenues and Streets far, far below.

One of the major attractions is the Wine List which is magnificent and very reasonably priced. Some of the rarer wines (such as a 1971 Chateau Leoville Lascases) actually costs less here than at the retailers. Their 'extensive' lists runs to twenty-two pages. I chose a Corton, Chanson '69 from Burgundy because I am a devotee of the pinot noir grape (used in Champagne). I love its inherent sensuality, its lush, velvety richness, which, I thought, would go well with our choice of Rack of Lamb prepared in the James Beard style. This was preceded by grilled Hawaiian blue Prawns in garlic oil over seaweed. Dessert specialities include Plum Terrine with walnut Croquante Icecream or a Banana and Caramel Tart with bitter chocolate mousse.

My advice to diners is, take time to study the Wine List, choose the wine and then decide on your choice of dish to complement the wine, and not the other way round.

Trim up your Waistline

A must for aspiring Slender Gourmets is 'The Hors d'Oeuvrerie', besides offering a selection of gastronomic appetizers from around the World, it also offers; jazz, dance, moonlight and romance.

You can watch International Chefs prepare their own national and regional dishes. Selections could include: Sate, Rumaki, Sushi, Sashimi, Barbecued Ribs, Dim Sum, Pizzella, Crab Fritters, Guacamole and Tapas, with which you create your own meal, whether it be a banquet or a more restrained selection.

A live Jazz combination plays sweet sophisticated music for listening or dancing to, a few shimmys, twists, rumba rolls, leg kicks, tummy contractions and tango leans soon works off any excess calories and tones up slack muscles.

Slender Gourmets know the motto: eat it on, exercise it off.

Le Cirque Restaurant at 58 East 65th Street, New York

Life is a Circus, a happy carousel, where everyone acts out his part, and what better place than a restaurant where one can go, to see and be seen.

Sirio Maccioni modestly describes his flower-filled, intimately elegant restaurant as 'really being a bistro'. Bistro-type conviviality flows; regular habitees from nearby millionaire residences on Park and Fifth Avenues, are friends and guests of Sirios. The seating is close enough for intimate conversation with either your own or guests at nearby tables. Immaculately dressed Anglo/French/American millionaires accompanied by fashionably thin, power-playing ladies are frequent diners. 'Le Cirque' is packed from 6.00 onwards with a constant stream of people coming and going, some perhaps only having one or two courses, or 'toying with a fork ladies' with nipped waistlines.

Chef de Cuisine Daniel Boulud has composed a lengthy, highly innovative Menu, specialities ranging from Littleneck Clams in Champagne Broth to the fabulous Crème Brulée du Cirque ou le Soufflé au Chocolat.

The famous 'Paul Bocuse' soup of Truffles, Vegetables and Foie Gras covered with a pastry lid which retains the delicate aromas and flavours, is utterly delicious and a Slender Gourmet recommendation. As is also paper thin sliced Carpaccio de Sea Bass served with Scallions, Eggplant and Arugula.

I was torn between the choice of entrées; the sauteed Veal Chop with sweet pimentos, pumpkin and green leaf Vegetable Strudel with Parmesan sounded particularly intriguing. Or a Mignonette of Beef Tenderloin with stuffed Marrow Bone and Baked Onions with balsamic vinegar. Sautéed Swordfish Goujonette with Artichokes, Pearl Onions, lemon juice and tarragon. Black Sea Bass wrapped in crispy Potatoes sitting on a bed of braised Leeks and served with a red wine sauce was another Slender Gourmet recommendation.

Le Cirque has achieved a mega-star combination of cuisine, service, ambience and patrons, regulars include Ronald Reagan, Ivana Trump and Roger Verge. A 'magic must' not to be missed in Manhattan, but do book at least a week in advance.

7 Take A Deep Breath

The problem with many sporting activities is that one has to be fit in order to 'keep fit' playing them.

Tennis and squash fall into this category. Golf and bowls are less energetic, but they barely reach the stomach muscles; rowing develops the chest, arms and shoulders and cycling enhances the calves.

Although these sports will tone you up most effectively, there are other gentler activities that should not be overlooked such as dancing, deep breathing and incidental exercise. For the more adventurous, as already suggested, why not try a trip in a hot air balloon or take up sailing?

Dancing

Disco has certain advantages over ballroom, a partner being superfluous, you can make your movements as energetic or casually elegant as you choose.

A good movement for Aspiring Slender Gourmets is the Hip Twist Step that works the hips and waist in all the right directions.

Hip Twist Step

Stand with your feet about a foot apart, toes facing front.
Point the ball of your right foot outwards to 3 o'clock.
Then turn the right foot inwards to face 9 o'clock.
Repeat eight times with the right foot, eight times with the left foot.
There are lots of variations you can develop from this one basic step.

Whether you are dancing at Maxim's or on your own at home, play your favourite piece of music whether it be disco, jazz, rock, soul or country, as long as it's got a good rhythmical beat that makes you want to move.

Give yourself space and *flow* ...

Start with the shoulders, making half circles back and forwards; then stretch the neck, cat-fashion, from side to side. Shake your arms and hands, give at the knees and finish off with the Hip Twist Step above. God bless America!

Breathe the Years and Pounds Away

Correct breathing is a pleasurable, non-exhausting activity especially when the air is fresh.

Air contains oxygen and we need oxygen to feed and cleanse the blood. This, in turn, travels throughout the body, revitalizing and nourishing every muscle, ligament, cellular tissue, organ, nerve and gland.

Deep breathing exercises the lungs, ribcage and the auxilliary muscles attached to the abdomen. These in turn massage the internal organs, helping the digestion and assimilation of food.

Yogis, who have worked out a complete health and exercise system based on deep-breathing techniques, believe that 'the more and deeper you breathe the younger you get'. If you can honestly say that you breathed deeper and better quality air the preceeding year why become a year older when you feel a year younger?

By following the Champagne Diet and breathing deeply you will be able physically to deduct a year (or two or three) next birthday.

A fact that people don't realize and what every Aspiring Slender Gourmet should know is that, apart from the years, the POUNDS can also be breathed away! The theory is that the process of metabolism is speeded up by an extra intake of oxygen.

Breathing Exercise No. 1. The Deep Breath, which benefits all parts.

BREATHE IN slowly and deeply, being aware of the ribcage expanding sideways as the lungs fill with life-giving oxygenated air.

BREATHE OUT just as slowly and deeply, being aware of the ribcage falling inwards as the old, polluted carbon dioxide leaves the body.

Breathing Exercise No. 2. The Dog Pant.

BREATHE *quickly,* IN *and* OUT, *through the mouth (as though you have been running and are out of breath).*

Combine this with quick, small tummy pulls, in and out.

Breathing Exercise No. 3. The Sitali Breath.

Place tongue between the lips so that just the tip protrudes.

BREATHE IN slowly through the mouth. Withdraw the tongue and close the lips.

BREATHE OUT slowly through the nostrils.

When proficient, add a stomach retraction.

At the end of BREATHING OUT withdraw the stomach inwards, towards the spine.

Incidental Exercising

These are exercises that can be done during the course of your daily round of activities, like walking short distances rather than using the car, using stairs instead of the lift and walking the escalators rather than riding them.

In Japan it is not unusual for businessmen and women to break into a two minute exercise session, sometimes on the hour, every hour, during the day.

At the sound of a bell everyone stops talking, stands up, bows politely to each other and goes through a few stretch and twist movements before resuming where they left off.

Small doses of frequent exercise are more effective than strenuous longer sessions tackled once a week. Simple tummy 'pull ins' with short 'hold' periods, for example, can be done whilst shaving, under the shower, having a bath, travelling, sitting at the desk, on the phone and in bed.

All these little two-three minute exercise breaks add up to double figures by the end of the day.

Speed up your Metabolism

One of my favourite spots for breathing fresh clean air, far away from polluted city streets and traffic fumes, is in a hot air balloon. Why not glide up, in a beautiful balloon, to the rarefied atmosphere of a thousand or so feet? Drifting lazily over hills, trees, meadows and lakes, the air sparkles with a crisp, fragrant freshness like that of a good Champagne. Take in lots of deep breaths and say to yourself 'I am breathing the POUNDS away'.

Hot air ballooning attracts a large number of enthusiasts who traditionally arrive with lots of bubbly.

In the old days three or four people would clamber into the basket taking the Champagne with them and use the bottles as ballast. After drinking the contents they would discard them to gain height (which is unkind to those on the ground whose property or person could get hit by falling glass).

These days most hot air balloon excursions are divided into two parties; those who go up in the balloon and those who follow the balloon's progress in a Champagne-filled Landrover.

When the balloon descends, often into a favoured flowerbed or, worse still, a field of nurturing crops, the wrath of the property owners has to be appeased somehow. At this point, the Landrover arrives, the butler jumps out and starts pulling the corks, a multi-explosion of pops, the balloonists, Landrover squad, horticulturalists and farmers are soon united in the joys of an impromptu Champagne party.

the rarefied atmosphere

A less exhilarating alternative to ballooning is to sit under a tree. Trees give off oxygen and obligingly take in the carbon dioxide that we breathe out, which is a convenient two-way exercise for both the breather and the tree.

Yachting is so Bracing ...

Whether you be sitting on the side of a sailing dinghy, feet braced against the gunnel, or standing on a wind-surfing board, the body acting as counter-balance to the wind and sails keeps the stomach muscles flexed ready for action, such as falling overboard, clambering back into the boat is excellent exercise.

By the way, if you are a yachting enthusiast and took part in one of the famous races such as the Admiral's Cup, which is sponsored by Mumm's Cordon Rouge Champagne, you could win your weight in bubbly! You'll also get the cheers and applause of the multitude which is good for the psyche. Think of it, thirteen or fourteen stone converted into bottles and magnums, even Jeroboams!

Champneys Health Club, Meridien Hotel, Piccadilly

It is a good idea to join a Health Club. One of the most luxurious in London is Champneys whose facilities include squash courts, a swimming pool complete with marbled nymphs, a fern-graced whirlpool and a gym equipped with the latest exercise machines.

After your fitness assessment test you could give yourself a leisurely workout and relaxation session, don a comfortable track suit and initiate yourself into exercise by 'spot-pacing' on the electronic treadmill? This moving carpet strip is monitored by a self-operated timer allowing you to decide whether to take a walk, trot, jog or break into a run.

Jogging, or any aerobic activity, strengthens the heart muscle and helps reduce the heart-attack risk, which means you have more years ahead in which to follow the Champagne life-style.

The Sit-Up Board, in the gym, is good for toning up and strengthening the stomach muscles. It's very popular as it allows you to be in a recumbent position, with your legs and hips raised half of the time. The other half is spent executing a series of sit-ups.

the winning skipper

Oh, hang it all ...

Hanging by the hands or feet, provided it's not the neck, is very good for you; it stretches the spine and gives the body that elegant, elongated El Greco look (as opposed to a Rubens cherub). An alternative to free-style hanging is a vertical board which clasps your body and can be adjusted to the angle of your choice. A couple of seconds, or minutes, with your head pointing to Australia is both physically and mentally stimulating, which is why some people do their best thinking standing on their heads.

Don't overdo the exercise; beginners should take it easily, interspersing physical activity with bouts of stretching and relaxing. Eventually you can join the more proficient and give your muscles something of a challenge.

The Aspiring Slender Gourmet should now have a swim around the Grecian marbled goddesses in the blue-mosaic-tiled pool. Twelve metres of warm blue water provide the space for an acquatic workout and when set in surroundings of cool, neoclassical splendour makes one feel either like a Roman Emperor or Venus rising from the sea.

Stepping into the whirlpool is by contrast, hot and peaceful, the only sound coming from jets of water releasing a steady stream of pulsating bubbles that caress and massage the shoulders and back, leading perhaps to thoughts of other bubbles that sing in the glass.

Facts about Abdominals

The old portraits of handsome generals surveying the scene of battle, with broad shoulders, neat waistlines and diminishing hips, often depended on a tightly laced corset to hold everything in. Nobody needs go to those uncomfortable lengths today, provided that they keep their own built-in muscular corset fully toned-up. Nature's corset is designed to hold the abdomen and its contents firmly in place for a lifetime of wear.

Your Corset

The abdominal corset is made up of muscles that go diagonally, horizontally and vertically over the stomach area. The upper part is flanked by the ribcage and the lower half by the pelvic bones. This muscular corset holds in not only the flesh but the abdominal contents as well. Think of it – fifty metres of intestine as well as heavy organs like the stomach, liver, bladder, pancreas and spleen. If this muscular corset slackens these contents can fall out of alignment, pushing against the abdominal wall, making a protuberance; but, worse still, if these organs are

The Whirlpool

squashed together minor and major health disorders develop, ranging from ulcers to severe cases of indigestion affecting the heart, pulmonary veins and arteries.

According to an article in the *British Medical Journal* people with *largesse* are regarded as high heart-attack and stroke risks. For health, fitness and appearance the stomach muscles are the most important ones to keep in first class condition.

Why, you may ask, do those surplus pounds always settle around the middle rather than build up on the legs, arms, chest or hips? It's because the abdomen, that fleshy area extending from the ribcage to the pelvic girdle is the part of the body that gets exercised the least.

You need special exercises to tone-up and strengthen the abdominals and that's why you should try and spend five to ten minutes every morning, and evening, doing the CHAMPAGNE QUARTET.

There is no need to suffer the discomfort of a chilly floor; instead, why not do them in the comfort and warmth of your bed? Exercising in bed is part of the Champagne luxury image.

THE CHAMPAGNE QUARTET

'Champagne Charlie is my name,
Champagne Drinking is my game ...
The Champagne Quartet is my aim ...'

The singer of this popular Edwardian Music Hall ballad would certainly have tried, provided there was sufficient inducement. Reward yourself with a bottle of your favourite when you have mastered the Quartet.

The exercises consist of: Half Sit-Ups
Waist Turns
Full Sit-Ups
The Champagne Challenge

Half-Sit-ups

Works lower abdominals

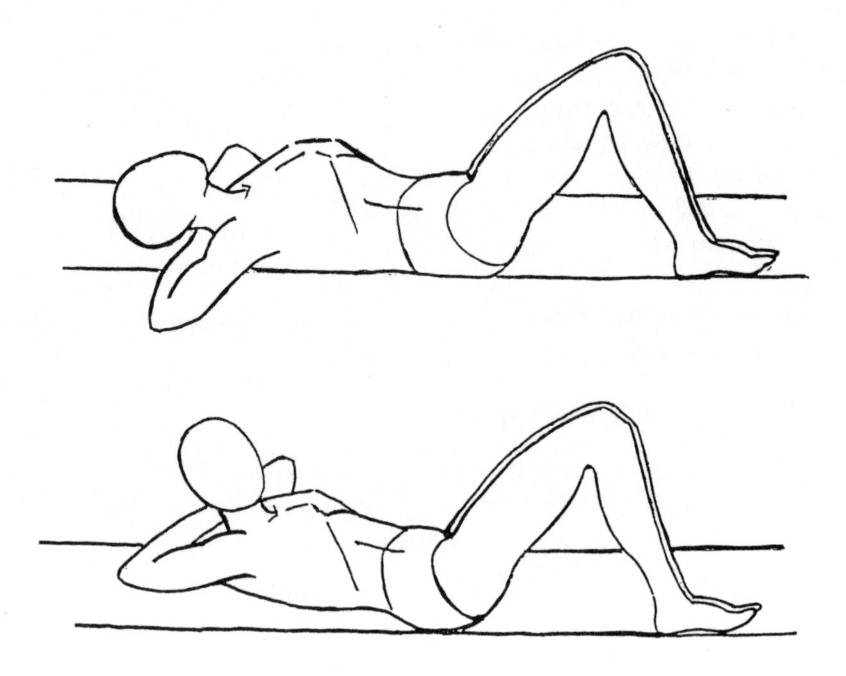

Push aside the pillows so that your head lies flat on the mattress. Link fingers, hands behind neck, elbows back. Bend knees, feet flat.

Lift your head and upper back, keeping your elbows parallel to the mattress. Lower body.

Start by doing 8 Slow – Pause, 12 Quick – Rest.

Increase the number of rounds when your stomach muscles say 'yes'.

WAIST TURNS

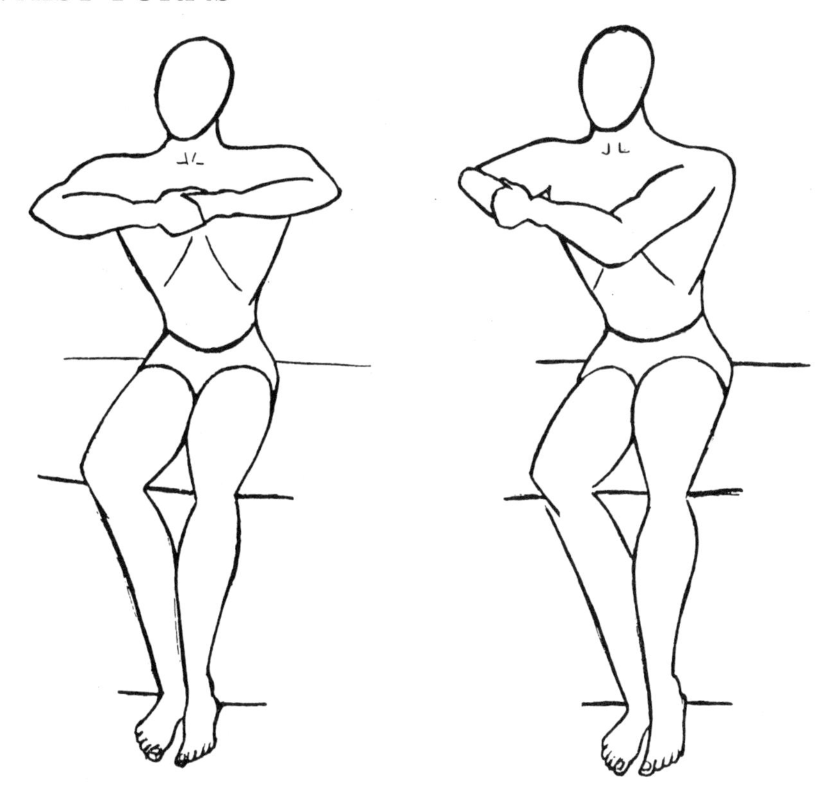

Sit on the edge of the bed for these turns and also for the Full Sit-Ups that follow.

Face front, arms folded, hold away from the body at chest level.

8 turns to the Right
8 turns to the Left
Then 6 each side, 4 and finally 2.

FULL SIT-UPS

Works lower and upper abdominals

The Easy Way – Easy because you can grip the edge of the bed with the back of your thighs and knees. This helps enormously.

Lie flat, arms overhead, swing up to a sitting position, bend forward, sit up, round back, like down.

Try 6 to start with then gradually increase the number of repetitions each week.

You may now be ready for:

The Champagne Challenge

Works all the stomach muscles, up, down across and verticals.
The 'Challenge' is hard, so save it until the other three become relatively easy.

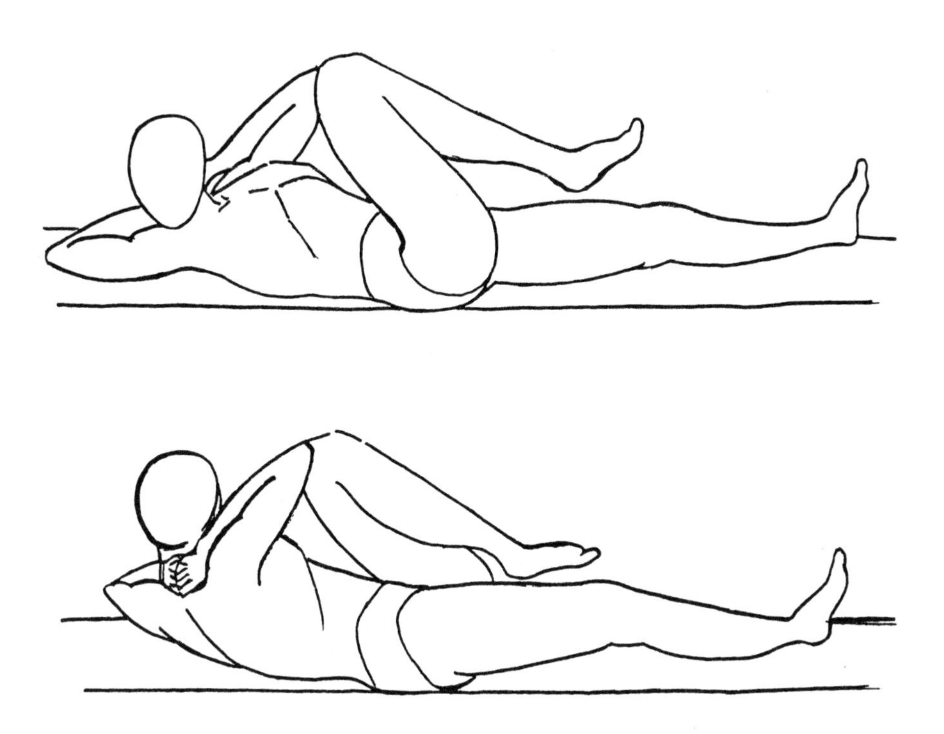

Lie flat. Clasp hands behind head, keep one leg straight the other knee bent in to the chest.

Lifting head and shoulders, touch right knee with left elbow and vice-versa.

Start by doing one round of 8, pause and ask yourself how you feel. Depending on the answer, you will get an idea as to how many rounds your body can do.

Set yourself a target – four, six, eight or ten rounds and when you succeed reach for your reward.

Champagne Posture

Whether you are standing, walking, sitting behind a desk or on a stool in your favourite Champagne bar, develop a relaxed yet alert posture.

Resist the downward pull of gravity by stretching upwards through the crown of the head. Make sure that your shoulders are relaxed.

Thinking tall makes you pull inwards from the waistband which immediately takes a couple of inches off the waist and stomach.

Good posture also injects your personality with a bon viveur sparkle and projects confidence and good health.

The Dangerous Plateau

You followed the Champagne Diet for a week or two, the scales indicated a weight loss of between two and five pounds, and then disaster struck, the scales would not budge.

Don't become discouraged and throw in the Champagne; you have hit the customary Dangerous Plateau, a period when the pounds will not diminish.

Take heart, the pounds may not be moving but the waistline inches are. The initial weight loss is mainly water and exercises build up muscle which weighs more than flesh; you may weigh the same but your shape will be firmer and slimmer.

Think Champagne Posture, pull away from your waistline and you may find you can tighten your belt by an extra notch.

This Dangerous Plateau period will pass within a couple of weeks, especially if you eat a little less and exercise a little more, you will resume your encouraging weight loss.

a scene from Dynasty

Envoi

You have lost what you set out to lose, the pounds (in weight & sterling) have been shed and the stomach muscles tightened. It's a fine figure which now smiles out at you from a full-length mirror. A reward is due and what better than the sybaritic indulgence of breakfast in bed, mid-morning.

Dress for the occasion in satin pyjamas or a negligee, refresh the pulse points with Guerlain's Dry Imperial, the Cologne that Napoleon III bathed with before going into battle.

As you will be sharing this event, hopefully with an adoring companion, the occasion calls for a little 'extra something', a jar of Beluga caviar sunk in a silver bowl filled with crushed ice, the moist blue-black eggs to be tantalizingly nibbled on delicate triangles of toast. Hot brioches would be succulent if their centres had been removed and replaced with warm foie gras. These little delicacies should be accompanied by a bottle of Louis Roederer, or even better, two bottles of Louis Roederer's Cristal, one on either side of the bed. Reaching across your partner to get the Champagne out of the ice bucket is good exercise for the arm, chest and torso.

Cristal, made from the finest grapes, was originally created for Tsar Alexander II of Russia who liked his Champagne bottles to be made out of pure crystal. The Champagne was named after the Tsar's choice of bottle.

The illustration might remind you of a scene from *Dynasty*, if it does, you're right, Alexis and Dex always have Champagne both sides of the bed just in case they get thirsty discussing oil leases.

This book has not only introduced you to the Champagne Diet but also to the Champagne Philosophy of Life. As a man of great style, but slender means, said with commendable dignity, as he savoured a glass of particularly elegant Henriot Cuvée Baccarat: 'He who drinks beer, thinks beer and, I am happy to say, I have never let a drop pass my lips.'